Ikenaga 2 Jos Leys

"A relatively simple formula can generate immensely complex images." – **Jos Leys**

Investigations

IN NUMBER, DATA, AND SPACE®

Implementing Investigations in Grade 3

PEARSON
Scott
Foresman

scottforesman.com

Editorial offices: Glenview, Illinois • Parsippany, New Jersey • New York, New York
Sales offices: Boston, Massachusetts • Duluth, Georgia
Glenview, Illinois • Coppell, Texas • Sacramento, California • Mesa, Arizona

T E R C

The Investigations Curriculum was developed by TERC, Cambridge, MA.

This material is based on work supported by the National Science Foundation ("NSF") under Grant No. ESI-0095450. Any opinions, findings, and conclusions or recommendations expressed in this material are those of the author(s) and do not necessarily reflect the views of the National Science Foundation.

ISBN: 0-328-24919-X
ISBN: 978-0-328-24919-0

Second Edition Copyright ©2008 Pearson Education, Inc.
All Rights Reserved. Printed in the United States of America. This publication is protected by Copyright, and permission should be obtained from the publisher prior to any prohibited reproduction, storage in a retrieval system, or transmission in any form by any means, electronic, mechanical, photocopying, recording, or otherwise. For information regarding permission(s), write to: Permissions Department, Scott Foresman, 1900 East Lake Avenue, Glenview, Illinois 60025.

1 2 3 4 5 6 7 8 9 10 V057 12 11 10 09 08 07

Co-Principal Investigators

T E R C

Susan Jo Russell

Karen Economopoulos

Authors

Lucy Wittenberg
Director Grades 3–5

Karen Economopoulos
Director Grades K–2

Virginia Bastable
(SummerMath for Teachers,
Mt. Holyoke College)

Katie Hickey Bloomfield

Keith Cochran

Darrell Earnest

Arusha Hollister

Nancy Horowitz

Erin Leidl

Megan Murray

Beth W. Perry

Susan Jo Russell

Deborah Schifter
(Educational
Development Center)

Kathy Sillman

Young Oh

Administrative Staff

Amy Taber
Project Manager

Beth Bergeron

Lorraine Brooks

Emi Fujiwara

Contributing Authors

Denise Baumann

Jennifer DiBrienza

Hollee Freeman

Paula Hooper

Jan Mokros

Stephen Monk
(University of Washington)

Mary Beth O'Connor

Judy Storeygard

Cornelia Tierney

Elizabeth Van Cleef

Carol Wright

Technology

Jim Hammerman

Classroom Field Work

Amy Appell

Rachel E. Davis

Traci Higgins

Julia Thompson

Collaborating Teachers

This group of dedicated teachers carried out extensive field testing in their classrooms, met regularly to discuss issues of teaching and learning mathematics, provided feedback to staff, welcomed staff into their classrooms to document students' work, and contributed both suggestions and written material that has been incorporated into the curriculum.

Bethany Altchek

Linda Amaral

Kimberly Beauregard

Barbara Bernard

Nancy Buell

Rose Christiansen

Chris Colbath-Hess

Lisette Colon

Kim Cook

Frances Cooper

Kathleen Drew

Rebeka Eston Salemi

Thomas Fisher

Michael Flynn

Holly Ghazey

Susan Gillis

Danielle Harrington

Elaine Herzog

Francine Hiller

Kirsten Lee Howard

Liliana Klass

Leslie Kramer

Melissa Lee Andrichak

Kelley Lee Sadowski

Jennifer Levitan

Mary Lou LoVecchio

Kristen McEnaney

Maura McGrail

Kathe Millett

Florence Molyneaux

Amy Monkiewicz

Elizabeth Monopoli

Carol Murray

Robyn Musser

Christine Norrman

Deborah O'Brien

Timothy O'Connor

Anne Marie O'Reilly

Mark Paige

Margaret Riddle

Karen Schweitzer

Elisabeth Seyferth

Susan Smith

Debra Sorvillo

Shoshanah Starr

Janice Szymaszek

Karen Tobin

JoAnn Trauschke

Ana Vaisenstein

Yvonne Watson

Michelle Woods

Mary Wright

Tiffany Young

Note: Unless otherwise noted, all contributors listed above were staff of the Education Research Collaborative at TERC during their work on the curriculum. Other affiliations during the time of development are listed.

Advisors

Deborah Lowenberg Ball,
University of Michigan

Hyman Bass, Professor of Mathematics and Mathematics Education
University of Michigan

Mary Canner, Principal, Natick Public Schools

Thomas Carpenter, Professor of Curriculum and Instruction,
University of Wisconsin-Madison

Janis Freckmann, Elementary Mathematics Coordinator,
Milwaukee Public Schools

Lynne Godfrey, Mathematics Coach,
Cambridge Public Schools

Ginger Hanlon, Instructional Specialist in Mathematics,
New York City Public Schools

DeAnn Huinker, Director, Center for Mathematics and
Science Education Research, University of Wisconsin-Milwaukee

James Kaput, Professor of Mathematics, University of
Massachusetts-Dartmouth

Kate Kline, Associate Professor, Department of Mathematics
and Statistics, Western Michigan University

Jim Lewis, Professor of Mathematics,
University of Nebraska-Lincoln

William McCallum, Professior of Mathematics,
University of Arizona

Harriet Pollatsek, Professor of Mathematics,
Mount Holyoke College

Debra Shein-Gerson, Elementary Mathematics Specialist,
Weston Public Schools

Gary Shevell, Assistant Principal,
New York City Public Schools

Liz Sweeney, Elementary Math Department,
Boston Public Schools

Lucy West, Consultant, Metamorphosis:
Teaching Learning Communities, Inc.

This revision of the curriculum was built on the work of the
many authors who contributed to the first edition (published
between 1994 and 1998). We acknowledge the critical
contributions of these authors in developing the content and
pedagogy of *Investigations*:

Authors

Joan Akers

Michael T. Battista

Douglas H. Clements

Karen Economopoulos

Marlene Kliman

Jan Mokros

Megan Murray

Ricardo Nemirovsky

Andee Rubin

Susan Jo Russell

Cornelia Tierney

Contributing Authors

Mary Berle-Carman

Rebecca B. Corwin

Rebeka Eston

Claryce Evans

Anne Goodrow

Cliff Konold

Chris Mainhart

Sue McMillen

Jerrie Moffet

Tracy Noble

Kim O'Neil

Mark Ogonowski

Julie Sarama

Amy Shulman Weinberg

Margie Singer

Virginia Woolley

Tracey Wright

PART 1

Collaborating with the Authors

Goals and Guiding Principles   1

The Teacher-Student-Curriculum Partnership   1

How *Investigations* Supports the
  Teacher's Role   2

PART 2

Using *Investigations*

Components of the Program   4

The Curriculum Units   6

Setting Up the *Investigations* Classroom   10

PART 3

Mathematics in Grade 3

Number and Operations: Whole Numbers   14

Number and Operations: Rational Numbers   18

Patterns, Functions, and Change   18

Data Analysis   20

Geometry and Measurement   21

PART 4

Ten-Minute Math and Classroom Routines

Preview   24

Ten-Minute Math: Counting Around the Class   25

Ten-Minute Math: Guess My Rule   26

Ten-Minute Math: More or Less?   28

Ten-Minute Math: Practicing Place Value   29

Ten-Minute Math: Quick Images   32

Ten-Minute Math: Today's Number   35

Ten-Minute Math: What Time Is It?   36

Classroom Routine: Class Collection   38

Classroom Routine: What's the Temperature?   40

PART 5

Technology in *Investigations*

Preview   43

Using Calculators with the Curriculum   43

Introducing and Managing the *LogoPaths*
  Software in Grade 3   44

Contents

PART 6

Professional Development

Teacher Notes in *Investigations*	47
Computational Fluency and Place Value	48
Computational Algorithms and Methods	52
Representations and Contexts for Mathematical Work	55
Foundations of Algebra in the Elementary Grades	60
Discussing Mathematical Ideas	65
Racial and Linguistic Diversity in the Classroom: What Does Equity Mean in Today's Math Classroom?	68
Titles of Grade 3 Teacher Notes by Unit	74

PART 7

Working with the Range of Learners: Classroom Cases

Preview	76
Summary of Cases	77
Setting Up the Mathematical Community	78
Accommodations for Learning	86
Language and Representation	97

PART 8

Grade 3 Scope and Sequence   103

NCTM Curriculum Focal Points and Connections   130

PART 9

Grade 3 Math Terms and Index   132

PART 1

Collaborating with the Authors

Goals and Guiding Principles

Investigations in Number, Data, and Space is a K–5 mathematics curriculum designed to engage students in making sense of mathematical ideas. Six major goals guided the development of this curriculum. The curriculum is designed to

- Support students to make sense of mathematics and learn that they can be mathematical thinkers.

- Focus on computational fluency with whole numbers as a major goal of the elementary grades.

- Provide substantive work in important areas of mathematics—rational numbers, geometry, measurement, data, and early algebra—and connections among them.

- Emphasize reasoning about mathematical ideas.

- Communicate mathematics content and pedagogy to teachers.

- Engage the range of learners in understanding mathematics.

Underlying these goals are three guiding principles that are touchstones for the *Investigations* team as we approach both students and teachers as agents of their own learning:

1. *Students have mathematical ideas.* Students come to school with ideas about numbers, shapes, measurements, patterns, and data. If given the opportunity to learn in an environment that stresses making sense of mathematics, students build on the ideas they already have and learn about new mathematics they have never encountered. They learn mathematical content and develop fluency and skill that is well grounded in meaning. Students learn that they are capable of having mathematical ideas, applying what they know to new situations, and thinking and reasoning about unfamiliar problems.

2. *Teachers are engaged in ongoing learning* about mathematics content, pedagogy, and student learning. The curriculum provides material for professional development, to be used by teachers individually or in groups, that supports teachers' continued learning as they use the curriculum over several years. The *Investigations* curriculum materials are designed as much to be a dialogue with teachers as to be a core of content for students.

3. *Teachers collaborate with the students and curriculum materials* to create the curriculum as enacted in the classroom. The only way for a good curriculum to be used well is for teachers to be active participants in implementing it. Teachers use the curriculum to maintain a clear, focused, and coherent agenda for mathematics teaching. At the same time, they observe and listen carefully to students, try to understand how they are thinking, and make teaching decisions based on these observations.

The Teacher-Student-Curriculum Partnership

Mathematics teaching and learning at its best is a collaboration among teachers, students, and the curriculum. Both the teacher and the curriculum contribute to this partnership in important ways. The curriculum materials provide a coherent, carefully sequenced core of mathematics content for students and supportive professional development material for teachers. Teachers are active partners in learning the curriculum well, understanding how each mathematical focus is developed, and implementing the curriculum in a way that accommodates the needs of their particular students.

The *Investigations* curriculum was field-tested in many different classrooms, representing a range of students and teachers, over several years. Thousands of hours of classroom observation, documentation, analysis of student work, and meetings with teachers were involved. Activities and the way they are presented to students were revised again and again.

Each time a curriculum unit was tested in a classroom, no matter how many times it had been tried and revised before, there was always more to discover about how students learn and how activities can be revised and modified to support them. This process, we have come to believe, can be endless. Just as you, a classroom teacher, learn more about students' learning each year, so do those of us who develop the curriculum. At some point we decide that, considering all the evidence, the curriculum has been sufficiently tested and works well for a wide range of students.

This lengthy and detailed process has resulted in a coherent core curriculum that is based on the real needs of real students and teachers. The process has also provided ample evidence that the collaboration of the teacher is essential. Only the teacher can understand and support the particular learning needs of a particular class of students in a particular school year. Only the teacher is present every day in the classroom, observing students' work, listening to their discourse, and developing an understanding of their mathematical ideas by analyzing what they say and do. In mathematics, as in any subject, only the teacher can continually assess students' strengths and needs and think through how best to accommodate differences to involve all students in substantive and challenging work.

How *Investigations* Supports the Teacher's Role

Modifying the curriculum and making it work in your classroom requires knowing the curriculum well. It means taking the time to understand the mathematics focus of each lesson and how the mathematical ideas build over many lessons. Learning the curriculum well means holding back the urge to change activities because you think they are too easy or too difficult for your students before you have tried them and actually seen your students' work. Keep in mind that the way ideas are developed and sequenced has been researched and tested in multiple classrooms, and many suggestions for accommodations are already built into the curriculum. Teachers tell us that they generally follow the curriculum as it is written the first year, and that they learn a great deal when activities that they thought would not work with their students turn out to be crucial to student learning.

You are an active partner in this teacher-student-curriculum partnership, and the curriculum must support your complex job by providing information about mathematics content and student learning. From the beginning, our intention in developing *Investigations* has been to create a professional development tool for teachers—a tool that provides opportunities for learning about mathematics content, how students learn, and effective pedagogy. Our design focuses as much on the teacher as learner as on the student as learner.

Two sections at the beginning of each curriculum unit, Mathematics in This Unit and Assessment in This Unit, provide an overview of the mathematics content, Math Focus Points, and benchmarks for student learning. The Math Focus Points for each session and the assessment benchmarks tell the mathematical story line of each curriculum unit so that you can productively guide students' work. Math Focus Points make explicit the purposes of the activities in each session and help you make choices about how to guide discussions. The assessment benchmarks for each curriculum unit are an aid in determining priorities and interpreting students' work.

The "teacher talk" printed in blue in each session is also an aid for focusing an activity and choosing questions to ask. It is not a script for how to address your students; it is a guide based on classroom experience with different ways of talking about mathematical ideas, introducing activities, and asking effective questions.

Teacher Notes collected at the end of each curriculum unit focus on key mathematical ideas and how students learn them. Because having students reason about, articulate, and justify their ideas is such a central part of the curriculum,

Dialogue Boxes provide examples of student discussion and teachers' efforts to focus this discussion. Additionally, examples of what students might say in class appear within the session descriptions.

To further support your work with the curriculum, this *Implementing Investigations in Grade 3* book provides an overview of the math content for the entire year (Part 3), a set of Teacher Notes that applies to the curriculum as a whole (Part 6), and a set of classroom cases written by teachers that provides examples of how they work with the range of learners in their classrooms (Part 7).

Teachers who use the *Investigations* curriculum over several years find that, as they teach a curriculum unit more than once, they gradually read more and more of the supporting material and incorporate it into their work with students. Teachers also use features such as the Teacher Notes and Dialogue Boxes as part of grade-level study groups or within other professional development structures. The better you know the curriculum and your students, the more you can internalize the mathematics focus and sequence and the better decisions you can make to support your students' learning.

Components of the Program

Curriculum Units

The curriculum at each grade level is organized into nine units (seven for kindergarten). These curriculum units are your teaching guides for the program. The unit organization is further described in the next section, "Using the Curriculum Units."

The curriculum units in Grade 3 offer from $2\frac{1}{2}$ to 5 weeks of work, each focused on the area of mathematics identified in the unit's subtitle.

This pacing is based on a school year that starts in early September, ends in late June, and has vacation weeks in February and April. The pacing will vary according to school calendars but may also vary depending on the needs of students, the school's years of experience with this curriculum, and other local factors.

Grade 3 Curriculum Units

Unit	Title	Number of Sessions	Suggested Pacing
1	**Trading Stickers, Combining Coins** Addition, Subtraction, and the Number System 1	17	September
2	**Surveys and Line Plots** Data Analysis	20	October–early November
3	**Collections and Travel Stories** Addition, Subtraction, and the Number System 2	26	Early November–December
4	**Perimeter, Angles, and Area** 2-D Geometry and Measurement	17	January
5	**Equal Groups** Multiplication and Division	23	February–early March
6	**Stories, Tables, and Graphs** Patterns, Functions, and Change	15	March
7	**Finding Fair Shares** Fractions and Decimals	14	April
8	**How Many Hundreds? How Many Miles?** Addition, Subtraction, and the Number System 3	19	May
9	**Solids and Boxes** 3-D Geometry and Measurement	13	June

The curriculum units are designed for use in the sequence shown. Each succeeding unit builds on the previous unit, both within and across strands. For example, the three units that focus on addition and subtraction (Units 1, 3, and 8) develop a sequence of ideas across the three units. Across strands, both Unit 6 (Patterns, Functions, and Change) and Unit 9 (3-D Geometry and Measurement) build on the ideas about multiplication that are first developed in Unit 5 but with new contexts.

Resources Binder

A binder for each grade level contains the reproducible Resource Masters and Transparencies that support your classroom instruction. These are also available on a CD. The binder also includes a CD with the *LogoF* appropriate to a particular grade level. The u materials for particular Investigations is spec curriculum units.

Investigations Software

LogoPaths Software for Grade 3 provides an e which students investigate movement along p perimeter, angle, and the characteristics of a va This software is provided as a disk to be used *Perimeter, Angles, and Area,* and is also availabl Scott Foresman Web site.

Student Activity Book

A booklet accompanying each curriculum uni consumable pages for student work, including in-class work, game recording sheets, and all pages for daily practice and for homework. The Student Activity Book is also available as a single volume, with all the curriculum units in

Student Math Handbook

A single handbook for each grade level in Grades 1–5 offers a valuable reference to the math words and ideas introduced in the curriculum units, as well as instruction pages for playing all the games. This book is designed to be used flexibly: as a resource for students during class work, as a book students can take home for reference while doing homework and playing math games with their families, and/or as a reference for families to better understand the work their children are doing in class.

Manipulatives Kit

A kit of materials is coordinated with the activities and games at each grade level. The Grade 3 kit includes class sets of the following items:

Connecting cubes

Pattern blocks

Wooden geometric solids

Straws and twist ties, for building 2-D and 3-D shapes

Color tiles

Wooden 1-inch cubes

Demonstration clock and student clocks

Blank cubes and labels, for making number cubes

Coin sets (pennies, nickels, dimes, quarters, half dollars, dollars)

Paper dollar bills

Metersticks/yardsticks

Indoor/outdoor thermometer

Class number line

Class 100 chart

Mirrors, for work with symmetry

Rulers (centimeters and inches)

Twist ties

Overhead tools: transparent counters, color tiles, pattern blocks, and coin sets

manipulatives should be accessible. Students should be able to make choices about what they need.

They are resources — learning supports.

Cards in Card Kit

Manufactured cards are used with some of the activities and games at each grade level. The cards for Grade 3 are as follows:

Digit Cards

Grade 3 Array Cards

Collection Cards

Implementing Investigations in Grade 3

At each grade level, this guide to implementing *Investigations* includes an overview of the curriculum; suggestions for using the curriculum units in your classroom; a closer look at the mathematics content of that particular grade, including lists of the Math Focus Points for each curriculum unit; program-wide Teacher Notes that explain some key ideas underlying the curriculum; and a set of case studies about working with a range of learners that can be used for professional development.

The Curriculum Units

The curriculum unit is your main teaching tool. It is your blueprint for the sequence and purpose of the daily lessons; it also contains guidelines for assessment, suggestions for differentiating instruction, and professional development materials to support your teaching.

Structure of a Curriculum Unit

Each curriculum unit is divided into Investigations. An Investigation focuses on a set of related mathematical ideas, coordinating students' work in hands-on activities, written activities, and class discussions over a period of several days.

Investigations are divided into one-hour *sessions,* or lessons. Sessions include the following features:

- *Math Focus Points:* This list of what students will be doing mathematically highlights the goals of each session.

- *Activities:* A session contains from one to three activities, organized as work for the whole class, pairs, small groups, or individuals.

- *Discussion:* Many sessions include whole-class time during which students compare methods and results and share conclusions. A subset of the session's Math Focus Points helps you guide each discussion.

- *Math Workshop:* In some sessions, students work in a Math Workshop format. Individually, in pairs, or in small groups, they choose from and cycle through a set of related activities. This setup is further discussed in a later section, "All About Math Workshop" (pp. 11–13).

- *Assessment:* Students are assessed through both written activities and observations; see "Assessment in This Unit" for further information.

- *Session Follow-Up:* Homework is provided for 2–3 days per week at Grade 3. In addition, each session includes a page for Daily Practice. These pages offer either ongoing review of materials from previous curriculum units or directed practice of content in the current curriculum unit. They can be used either for additional homework or for in-class practice. Relevant pages in the *Student Math Handbook* are also referenced here.

Your Math Day

The *Investigations* curriculum assumes that you spend 1 hour of each classroom day on mathematics, in addition to conducting brief Classroom Routines and Ten-Minute Math activities (further described later in this section and in Part 4 of this book). A chart called Today's Plan appears at the beginning of each session, laying out the suggested pacing for the activities in that 1-hour session. While you may need to adapt this structure to your particular classroom needs, be aware that it is important to move through all the activities because they are carefully designed to offer continued work on the key mathematical ideas. It is also essential that you allow time for class discussions, where students have an opportunity to articulate their own ideas, compare solutions, and consolidate understanding. See Teacher Note: Discussing Mathematical Ideas on pages 65–67 for further information on the importance of these class discussions.

Differentiated Instruction

Within the sessions, you will regularly see a feature titled "Differentiation: Supporting the Range of Learners." This feature offers ideas for intervention or extensions related to the particular work of that session. Ideas for helping English language learners are offered at the beginning of the curriculum unit and where applicable in the sessions. In addition, Part 7 of this book, "Working with the Range of Learners: Classroom Cases," presents situations from actual *Investigations* classrooms and invites you to consider how these case studies can inform your own teaching practice.

Ten-Minute Math and Classroom Routines

These brief activities, described in a box below Today's Plan for each session, require 10–15 minutes of additional daily work outside of math time. These routines and activities, an important part of the *Investigations* curriculum, offer ongoing skill building, practice, and review that support the regular math work; they also reinforce the work students have done in previous curriculum units and help students increase their repertoire of strategies for mental calculation and problem solving. Part 4 of this book, "Ten-Minute Math and Classroom Routines," provides detailed explanations of the activities to plan for Grade 3.

Assessment in This Unit

Opportunities for assessment are carefully woven throughout the curriculum units. A section at the beginning of each curriculum unit identifies the benchmarks students will be

expected to meet and specifies key activities you can observe, as well as the particular assessment activities where students will produce written work for your review. The final session in each curriculum unit is devoted to the End-of-Unit Assessment. Each written assessment in the curriculum unit is accompanied by a Teacher Note that provides examples of student work and guidelines that help you assess whether your students are meeting the benchmarks. For observed assessments, an assessment checklist is provided; here you can record notes about what students understand as you observe them engaged in the session's activities.

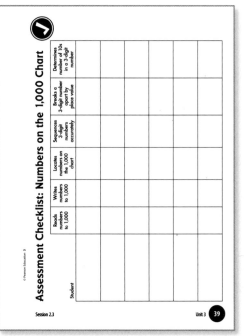

▲ An example of an Assessment Checklist

"Ongoing Assessment: Observing Students at Work" is a regular feature of the sessions. It identifies the particular math focus and lists questions for you to consider as you observe your students solving problems, playing math games, and working on activities. Teacher observations are an important part of ongoing assessment. Although individual observations may be little more than snapshots of a student's experience with a single activity, when considered together over time, they can provide an informative and detailed picture. These observations can be useful in documenting and assessing a student's growth and offer important sources of information when preparing for family conferences or writing student reports.

You may want to develop a system to record and keep track of your observations of students. The most important aspect of a record-keeping system is that it be both manageable and useful for you. Some teachers use systems such as the following:

- Jot down observations of students' work on a class list of names. Because the space is somewhat limited, it is not possible to write lengthy notes; however, when kept over time, these short observations provide important information.

- Place stick-on address labels on a clipboard. Take notes on individual students and then peel these labels off and put them in a file for each student.

- Jot down brief notes at the end of each week. Some teachers find that this is a useful way of reflecting on the class as a whole, on the curriculum, and on individual students. Planning for the next week's activities can benefit from these weekly reflections.

Observation checklists, student work on written assessments, and other examples of students' written work can be collected in a portfolio. Suggestions for particular work that might be saved in a portfolio are listed at the beginning of each curriculum unit, under "Assessment in This Unit."

Professional Development

One guiding principle of the *Investigations* curriculum is to provide support that helps teachers improve their own understanding of the mathematics that they are teaching and the learning that they observe in their students. To this end, the following materials are included in the curriculum for teachers' professional development:

- *Mathematics in This Unit:* An essay at the beginning of each curriculum unit explains in detail the Mathematical Emphases of the unit, the Math Focus Points related to each area of emphasis, and the work students will be doing in each area.

- *Algebra Connections in This Unit:* This essay, appearing in each of the number and operations units and in the patterns, functions, and change units, explains how the activities and ideas of the curriculum unit are laying a foundation for students' later work with algebra.

- *Math Notes, Teaching Notes, and Algebra Notes:* Found in the margins of the sessions, these brief notes provide information about mathematics content or student thinking, as well as teaching tips to help teachers better understand the work of that session.

- *Teacher Notes:* These essays, collected at the end of each curriculum unit, provide further practical information about the mathematics content and how students learn it. Many of the notes were written in response to questions from teachers or to discuss important issues that arose in field-test classrooms. They offer teachers help with thinking about mathematical ideas that may be unfamiliar to them; they also provide guidance for observing and assessing students' work.

- *Dialogue Boxes:* Also at the end of each curriculum unit are Dialogue Boxes that reflect classroom scenarios related to the activities of the unit. Since these Dialogue Boxes are based on actual teacher-student interactions, you learn how students typically express their mathematical ideas, what issues and confusions arise in their thinking, and how some teachers have chosen to guide particular class discussions.

Working with Families

Families are important partners with schools in the process of teaching mathematics. Because the teaching of mathematics has been evolving, many families may be unfamiliar with the approaches taken by the *Investigations* curriculum. For this reason, a number of Family Letters are provided. In Grade 3, these letters include the following:

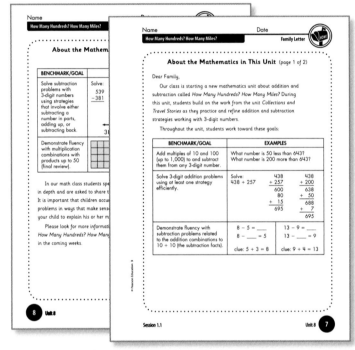

▲ **An example of a Family Letter**

- The first Family Letter in each curriculum unit, About the Mathematics in This Unit, introduces families to the mathematics that their children will be doing and to the benchmarks for that unit.

- A second letter in each curriculum unit, Related Activities to Try at Home, is sent home a few days after the first. It suggests related activities that families can do together and children's books that support students' work in mathematics.

- An additional letter provided in the first curriculum unit of the year, About Mathematics Homework, gives suggestions for helping students with their homework by establishing a regular time for homework, setting up a good working environment, and asking productive questions.

- Particular to Grade 3, two Family Letters focus on the ways students are learning their addition and multiplication combinations (facts) and how parents can support this work at home. The letter on Practicing Addition Combinations is provided with Unit 1, *Trading Stickers, Combining Coins;* the letter on Practicing Multiplication Combinations is provided with Unit 5, *Equal Groups.*

The *Student Math Handbook* is another valuable tool for working with families. The Math Words and Ideas section of this book provides an overview of the year's mathematics work, a closer look at the ideas and the kinds of problems students encounter, examples of student solutions, and questions that families and students can talk about together. The Handbook also contains game directions for use at school or at home.

Setting up the *Investigations* Classroom

As you begin using the *Investigations* curriculum, you may find yourself making decisions about how to set up the tables and chairs in your classroom and where to keep your materials. Students will at various times need to work individually, in pairs or small groups, and as a whole class. When working in pairs or small groups, they need to be able to see one another's work and listen to one another's ideas. Bringing students together for whole-group discussion is also a regular feature of the curriculum, and during these discussions it is important that students can easily see and hear one another. Ways of making this work are further discussed in the Teacher Note: Discussing Mathematical Ideas, on pages 65–67. You must also find ways to make materials and games easily accessible and consider how to organize the room for Math Workshops.

Materials as Tools for Learning

In an active mathematics classroom, certain basic materials should be available at all times: connecting cubes, pencils, blank paper, graph paper, calculators, things to count with, and measuring tools. Some activities in the curriculum require glue sticks and scissors or tape. Stick-on notes and large paper for posters are also useful materials.

So students can independently get what they need at any time, they should know where these materials are kept, how they are stored, and how they need to be returned to the storage area. For example, connecting cubes are best stored in towers of 10 and should be replaced in these towers when an activity is completed.

Rationale

Tools and materials are used throughout the *Investigations* curriculum. Students of all ages benefit from being able to use materials to model problems and explain their thinking.

It is important to encourage all students to use tools and materials, such as pattern blocks, geometric solids, connecting cubes, rulers, and coin sets. If materials are used only when someone is having difficulty, students may get the mistaken idea that using materials is a less sophisticated and less valued way of solving a problem. Encourage students to talk about how they used certain materials. They should see how different people, including the teacher, use a variety of materials in solving the same problem.

The more available materials are, the more likely students are to use them. Having materials available means that they are readily accessible to students and that students are allowed to make decisions about which tools to use and when to use them. In much the same way as you choose the best tool to use for certain projects or tasks, students should be encouraged to think about which material best meets their needs.

Using materials in the classroom may be a new experience for many students and teachers. Before introducing new materials, think about how you want students to use and care for them, including how they will be stored.

Introducing a New Material

Students need time to explore a new material before using it in structured activities. By freely exploring with new materials, students will discover many of the important characteristics of the new material and will gain some understanding of when it might make sense to use it. Although some free exploration should be done during regular math time, many teachers make materials, such as pattern blocks and geometric solids, available to students during free time or before or after school.

Plan for how materials will be cleaned up at the end of each class. Most teachers find that stopping 5 minutes before the end of class gives students time to clean up materials, organize and turn in their work, and double-check the floor for any stray materials.

Storing Materials

Store materials where they are easily accessible to students. Many teachers store materials in plastic tubs or shoe boxes arranged on a bookshelf or along a windowsill. In addition to pattern blocks, rulers, and connecting cubes, items such as calculators, coins, 100 charts, and paper (blank and grid) are important mathematical tools that should be available to students.

Games in the *Investigations* Curriculum

The games included in this curriculum are a central part of the mathematics in each curriculum unit, not just an enrichment activity. Games are used to develop concepts and to practice skills, such as learning to sort and classify polygons, finding combinations that make 100, or combining fractions. The rationale for using games is as follows:

• Games provide engaging opportunities for students to deepen their understanding of the number system and operations and to practice computation.

• Playing games encourages strategic mathematical thinking as students find an optimal way (rather than just any way) of "winning" the game.

• Games provide repeated practice without requiring the teacher to provide new problems.

• While students are playing the games, the teacher is free to observe students or to work with individuals or small groups.

Before introducing a game to students, it is important that you play the game for yourself to learn the mathematical ideas that students encounter as they play the game. For some games, variations are offered. Before using these variations, or any others you might think of, consider how changing the rules of the game changes the mathematical ideas with which students are working.

Games are often played frequently throughout a curriculum unit. Once games have been introduced, consider leaving them out throughout the year for students to play. It is expected that students will play a game many times as they develop fluency with numbers, computation, and geometry.

▲ An example of game instructions

▲ An example of a game recording sheet

All About Math Workshop

Math Workshop provides an opportunity for students to work on a variety of activities that focus on similar mathematical content. Math Workshops are found in most of the curriculum units and generally alternate with whole-class activities. Math Workshop is designed with two purposes in mind:

1. To give students an opportunity to develop and practice the concepts and skills being learned

2. To give the teacher time to work one-on-one or with small groups of students

During Math Workshop, students are also engaged in other key aspects of their school experience: making choices, planning their time, and taking responsibility for their own learning.

The activities in Math Workshop are not sequential; as students move among them, they continually revisit the important concepts and ideas they are learning. By repeatedly playing a game, or solving similar problems, students are able to refine strategies, use different contexts, and bring new knowledge to familiar experiences.

Setting Up Math Workshop

Organizing Materials Some teachers prefer to have Math Workshop activities set up at centers or stations around the classroom. At each center, students find the materials needed to complete the activity. Other teachers prefer to have materials stored in a central location and have students bring the materials to their desks or tables. You may find that you need to experiment with a few different structures before finding a setup that works best for you and your students. Materials should be readily accessible to students, and students should be expected to take responsibility for cleaning up and returning materials to their appropriate storage locations. Giving students a "5 minutes until cleanup" warning before the end of an activity session allows them to finish what they are working on and prepare for the upcoming transition, which is often to a class discussion.

Organizing the Students Each Math Workshop generally includes three to five activities that students do over several class sessions. Support students in organizing their time to complete the activities. Initially you may need to help students plan what they do and in what order, but as the year goes on, students should learn to make their choices, get their materials, engage with an activity for enough time to benefit from it, and then switch activities, without your help.

Often when a new activity is introduced, many students want to do it first. Assure them that they will be able to work on each activity. Some students may want to return to the same activity over and over again, such as a game, without trying other activities. Make sure these students do a different activity first, and then choose the favorite activity as a second choice. Other students may need to be encouraged to use their time efficiently to complete all activities. You may want to limit the number of students who work on a Math Workshop activity at one time. In some cases, the quantity of materials available limits the number of students who can do an activity at any one time. In others, limiting the number of students at one activity gives them the opportunity to work in smaller groups and requires students to make choices among activities.

We do not recommend that you organize students into groups and have each group at each activity for a set amount of time. While this method ensures that each student engages in each activity, it does not provide the flexibility and differentiation needed in the classroom. One student may have accomplished a task and need to move to a different activity, while another may be engaged in good mathematical work at a particular activity for a longer time. For the same reason, we also do not recommend that you conduct Math Workshop activities as whole class activities, one after the other.

The Role of the Student

Establish clear guidelines when you introduce Math Workshop activities. Discuss students' responsibilities:

- Work on every activity at least once.

- Be productively engaged during Math Workshop.

- Ask questions of other students when you don't understand or feel stuck. (Some teachers establish the rule, "Ask two other students before me," which requires students to check with two peers before coming to the teacher for help.)

Students should also determine a method to keep track of their work. Some teachers list the choices for sessions on a chart, the board, or an overhead projector to help students keep track of what they need to do. As students finish an activity, they write it on a list and place any work they have done in their folders.

The Role of the Teacher

Establishing the Routine You will probably find that much of your time during the initial Math Workshops is spent circulating around the classroom helping students get settled into activities and monitoring the overall management of the classroom. Once routines are familiar and well established, students will become more independent and responsible for their work during Math Workshop. This will allow you to spend more concentrated periods of time observing the class as a whole or working with individuals and small groups.

Making Expectations Explicit The amount of work that students are expected to complete will vary from classroom to classroom. Some activities include extensions and additional problems for students who need further practice or extra challenge. Suggestions are also made in the Math Workshop activities and the "Supporting the Range of Learners" sections in the Math Workshop sessions. As students begin each Math Workshop, make certain students know which activities they are expected to complete.

Individual and Small Group Work Math Workshop allows teachers to observe and listen to students while they work. At times, you may want to meet with individual students, pairs, or small groups who might need help (or additional challenges). You may also want to focus on particular students in order to get a better sense of their math understanding. Recording your observations of students will help you keep track of how they are interacting with materials and solving problems.

Sometimes one of the Math Workshop activities is a formal observed assessment. This type of assessment provides an opportunity to assess students as they work on a set of problems or play a game. You can record your observations on the assessment checklist that is provided in the Resources Binder.

Number and Operations: Whole Numbers

Addition, Subtraction, and the Number System

In Grade 3, students build an understanding of the base-ten number system to 1,000 by studying the structure of 1,000 and using a base-ten context to represent the place value of two-digit and three-digit numbers. Students identify the hundreds digit as representing how many 100s are in the number, the tens digit as representing how many 10s, and the ones digit as representing how many 1s. They also break numbers into 100s, 10s, and 1s in different ways:

$137 = 1$ hundred, 3 tens, and 7 ones

$137 = 1$ hundred, 2 tens, and 17 ones

$137 = 13$ tens and 7 ones

$137 = 12$ tens and 17 ones

$137 = 11$ tens and 27 ones

. . .

In their work with numbers and operations in Grade 3, students focus particularly on addition and subtraction. Students solve addition and subtraction problems with two-digit and three-digit numbers, developing computation strategies that are built on adding and subtracting multiples of 10 and finding combinations that add to 100. Addition strategies include breaking the numbers apart and then either adding by place or adding on one number in parts. They also examine problems that lend themselves to changing the numbers to make them easier to add. Subtraction strategies include subtracting a number in parts, adding up, and subtracting back.

Addition Strategies

Adding by place
$$349 + 175 =$$

$$300 + 100 = 400$$

$$40 + 70 = 110$$

$$9 + 5 = 14$$

$$400 + 110 + 14 = 524$$

Adding on one number in parts
$$349 + 175 =$$

$$349 + 100 = 449$$

$$449 + 50 = 499$$

$$499 + 25 = 524$$

Changing the numbers
$$349 + 175 =$$

$$350 + 175 = 525$$

$$525 - 1 = 524$$

Subtraction Strategies

Subtracting in parts
$$451 - 187 =$$

$$451 - 100 = 351$$

$$351 - 80 = 271$$

$$271 - 7 = 264$$

Adding up
$$451 - 187 =$$

$$187 + \underline{13} = 200$$

$$200 + \underline{251} = 451$$

$$13 + 251 = 264$$

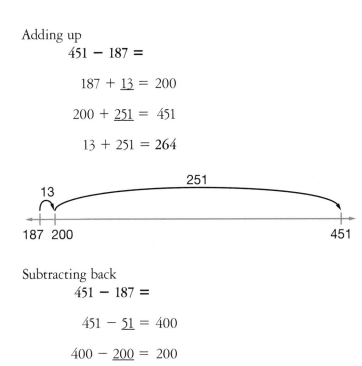

Subtracting back
$$451 - 187 =$$

$$451 - \underline{51} = 400$$

$$400 - \underline{200} = 200$$

$$200 - 13 = 187$$

$$51 + 200 + 13 = 264$$

Students expand their understanding of subtraction to include other problem situations besides removal (or take away)—the type they are probably most familiar with from their work in Grades K–2. These include comparison problems and finding the missing part of a whole:

> If I am collecting 1,000 baseball cards, and I have 250 so far, how many more do I need?

The ability to visualize what is happening in a subtraction situation is an important foundation for understanding the operation and how it works and for making good decisions about strategies for computation. Students build this understanding by using visual representations (cubes, number lines, 300 charts, and 1,000 charts) and story contexts. They work on developing fluency with subtraction problems related to the addition combinations up to $10 + 10$ (the subtraction facts) so they are able to use these easily when solving subtraction problems with two-digit and three-digit numbers.

The Algebra Connections page in each of the three curriculum units that focus on addition and subtraction shows how students are applying the commutative and associative properties of addition as they develop strategies for solving addition problems. These pages also highlight students' applications of the inverse relationship between addition and subtraction and how algebraic ideas underlie what students are doing when they create equivalent expressions in order to solve a problem (e.g., $48 + 72 = 50 + 70$)

Mathematical Emphases

The Base-Ten Number System

- Understanding the equivalence of one group and the discrete units that comprise it

- Extending knowledge of the number system to 1,000

Whole Number Operations

- Understanding different types of subtraction problems

- Describing, analyzing, and comparing strategies for adding and subtracting whole numbers

Computational Fluency

- Adding and subtracting accurately and efficiently

Benchmarks (compiled from Units 1, 3, and 8)

- Demonstrate fluency with the addition combinations up to 10 + 10.

- Add multiples of 10 (up to 100) to and subtract them from 2-digit and small 3-digit numbers.

- Solve addition problems with 2-digit numbers using strategies involving breaking numbers apart by place or adding one number in parts.

- Break up 3-digit numbers less than 200 into 100s, 10s, and 1s in different ways (e.g., 153 equals 1 hundred, 5 tens, and 3 ones; 15 tens and 3 ones; 14 tens and 13 ones; etc.).

- Find combinations of 2-digit numbers that add to 100 or $1.00.

- Read, write, and sequence numbers up to 1,000.

- Identify the value of each digit in a 3-digit number (100s, 10s, and 1s).

- Identify how many groups of 10 are in a 3-digit number (e.g., 153 has 15 groups of tens plus 3 ones).

- Solve addition problems with 3-digit numbers (up to 400) using strategies that involve breaking numbers apart, either by place value or by adding one number in parts.

- Solve subtraction story problems in contexts that include removing a part from a whole, comparing two quantities, or finding the missing part.

- Solve subtraction problems with 2-digit and 3-digit numbers (up to 300) using strategies that involve either subtracting a number in parts, adding up, or subtracting back.

- Add multiples of 10 and 100 (to 1,000) to and subtract them from any 3-digit number.

- Solve 3-digit addition problems using at least one strategy efficiently.

- Demonstrate fluency with subtraction problems related to the addition combinations to 10 + 10 (the subtraction facts).

- Solve subtraction problems with 3-digit numbers using strategies that involve either subtracting a number in parts, adding up, or subtracting back.

Multiplication and Division

Students investigate the properties of multiplication and division, including the inverse relationship between the two operations, and develop strategies for solving multiplication and division problems. Their work focuses on developing the idea that both multiplication and division involve a number of equal-sized groups.

Students are introduced to arrays—rectangular arrangements of objects in rows and columns—a visual image that supports their understanding of multiplication.

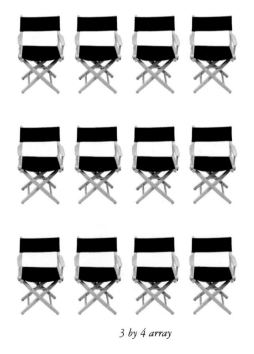

3 by 4 array

They use these rectangular arrays to represent the relationship between a product and its factors. Students determine, describe, and compare sets of multiples, noticing their characteristics and relationships, and use these to investigate important ideas about how multiplication works. They learn the multiplication combinations with products up to 50.

$$\underline{7} \times \underline{6} =$$

$$\underline{6} \times \underline{7} =$$

Start with

_____

$$\underline{4} \times \underline{5} =$$

$$\underline{5} \times \underline{4} =$$

Start with

_____

Students solve division situations that involve sharing ("Divide 35 pennies among 5 people equally. How many pennies does each person receive?") and those that involve grouping ("How many groups of 5 pennies can I make if I have 35 pennies?").

Sharing: Divide 35 pennies among 5 people equally. How many pennies are in each share?

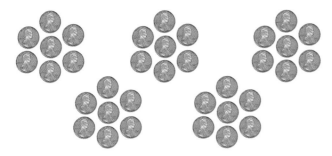

Grouping: How many groups of 5 pennies can I make if I have 35 pennies?

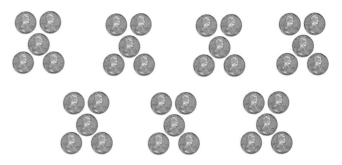

Students use their knowledge of the relationship between division and multiplication by reasoning in ways like the following: "I know that five 5s is 25, and two more 5s make 35, so I have 7 groups of 5." Students are also introduced to two forms of division notation—$35 \div 5$ and $5\overline{)35}$—and learn how to interpret these numbers and symbols in terms of the meaning and actions of division.

The Algebra Connections page in the curriculum unit that focuses on multiplication and division shows how students are applying the commutative and distributive properties of multiplication as they solve problems. It also highlights students' applications of the inverse relationship between multiplication and division.

Mathematical Emphases

Whole Number Operations

- Understanding the meaning of multiplication

- Reasoning about numbers and their factors and multiples

- Understanding and working with an array model of multiplication

- Developing strategies for division based on understanding the inverse relationship between multiplication and division

Computational Fluency

- Learning the multiplication combinations with products up to 50 fluently

Benchmarks

- Demonstrate an understanding of multiplication and division as involving groups of equal groups.

- Solve multiplication combinations and related division problems using skip counting or known multiplication combinations.

- Interpret and use multiplication and division notation.

- Demonstrate fluency with the multiplication combinations with products up to 50 (by the end of Grade 3).

Number and Operations: Rational Numbers

Students use a variety of contexts to understand, represent, and combine fractions. These include rectangles representing "brownies," hexagonal pattern block "cookies," and groups of objects.

fourths of a brownie   *halves of a cookie*   *thirds of a group*

Students work with halves, fourths, eighths, thirds, and sixths as they learn how fractions represent equal parts of a whole. They learn the meanings of the numerator and denominator of a fraction. Thus when comparing unit fractions (fractions with 1 as the numerator), they understand that the larger the denominator, the smaller the part of the whole: $\frac{1}{6}$ is smaller than $\frac{1}{2}$ of the same whole. Students also gain experience with common equivalencies, for example, that $\frac{3}{6}$ and $\frac{2}{4}$ are both equal to $\frac{1}{2}$. Using these equivalents in contexts, students find combinations of fractions that are equivalent to a whole or to another fraction. For example,

$$\frac{1}{2} + \frac{2}{6} + \frac{1}{6} = 1$$

$$\frac{1}{3} + \frac{1}{6} = \frac{1}{2}$$

Students are introduced to decimal fractions (0.05 and 0.25) within the context of money and gain familiarity with fractional and decimal equivalents involving halves and fourths.

Mathematical Emphases

- Understanding the meaning of fractions (halves, fourths, eighths, thirds, sixths) and decimal fractions (0.05, 0.25) as equal parts of a whole (an object, an area, a set of objects)

- Using representations to combine fractions (halves, fourths, eighths, thirds, and sixths)

Benchmarks

- Divide a single whole or a quantity into equal parts and name those parts as fractions or mixed numbers.

- Identify equivalent fractions $\left(\text{e.g., } \frac{3}{6} = \frac{1}{2} \text{ and } \frac{1}{3} = \frac{2}{6}\right)$.

- Find combinations of fractions that are equal to 1 and to other fractions $\left(\text{e.g., } \frac{3}{6} + \frac{1}{2} = 1; \frac{1}{6} + \frac{1}{6} = \frac{1}{3}; \text{ and } \frac{1}{3} + \frac{1}{6} = \frac{1}{2}\right)$.

Patterns, Functions, and Change

Students study situations of change as they examine temperature change over time in different places around the world, analyze number sequences generated by repeating patterns, and consider a fantasy situation in which children receive a certain number of *Magic Marbles* each day. They make, read, and compare line graphs that show a relationship between two variables in situations of change over time.

Students learn how to find the two values represented by a point on a coordinate graph by referring to the scales on the horizontal and vertical axes. Students focus on seeing a graph as a whole, think about the overall shape of a graph, and discuss what the overall shape shows about the change in the situation it represents. A class temperature graph is created over the course of the year and discussed regularly. Students learn to read and interpret temperatures using standard units.

Students also use tables as a representation that shows how one variable changes in relation to another variable. The emphasis is on how the numbers in the table relate to the situation they represent and to graphs of the same situation.

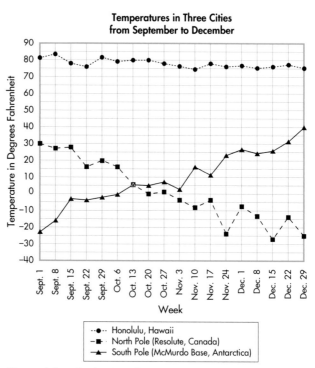

Line graph from Grade 3 Unit 6

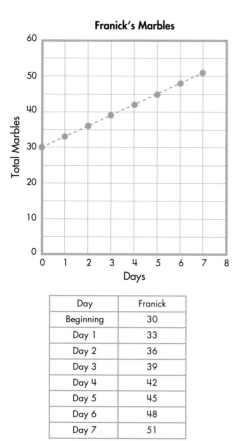

Day	Franick
Beginning	30
Day 1	33
Day 2	36
Day 3	39
Day 4	42
Day 5	45
Day 6	48
Day 7	51

Table and graph from Grade 3 Unit 6

Students use both tables and graphs to examine and compare situations with a constant rate of change. They examine the relationship between columns of the table and consider why the points on graphs representing such situations fall in a straight line. By examining tables and graphs, students consider any initial amount and the constant rate of change to develop general rules that express the relationship between two variables in these contexts.

Mathematical Emphases

Using Tables and Graphs

- Using graphs to represent change

- Using tables to represent change

Linear Change

- Describing and representing a constant rate of change

Number Sequences

- Constructing, describing, and extending number sequences with constant increments generated by various contexts

Measuring Temperature

- Understanding temperature and measuring with standard units

Benchmarks

- Interpret graphs of change over time, including both the meaning of points on the graph and how the graph shows that values are increasing, decreasing, or staying the same.

- Interpret temperature values (e.g., relate temperatures to seasons and to what outdoor clothing would be needed).

- Create a table of values for a situation with a constant rate of change and explain the values in the table in terms of the situation.

- Compare related situations of constant change by interpreting the graphs, tables, and sequences that represent those situations.

Data Analysis

Students collect, represent, describe, and interpret data. They work with both categorical and numerical data and consider how to examine a data set as a whole and make statements about the whole group. To make sensible statements about a categorical data set that has many different values, students group the data into categories that help them see the data as a whole. Students order numerical data by value so that they can see the shape of the data—where the data are concentrated, where they are spread out, which intervals have many pieces of data, and which have very few. They describe what values would be typical or atypical, based on the data, and compare data sets to develop a sense of how data can be useful in describing and comparing some characteristic of a group.

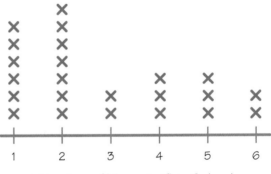

Number of Years in This School

Line plot from Grade 3 Unit 2

Students work with their own data, creating representations and then comparing and discussing these representations. Students use double bar graphs to compare groups, including some in which the scales have intervals greater than 1.

How Do You Get to School

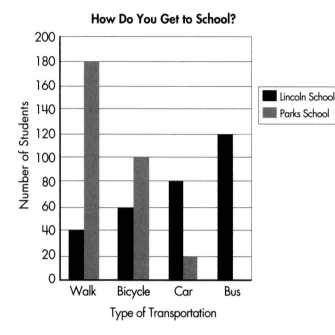

Double bar graph from Grade 3 Unit 2

Students interpret line plots and create their own line plots to represent numerical data. By conducting their own data investigations, students consider how the question they pose and the way they conduct their study affect the resulting data.

Mathematical Emphases

- Describing, summarizing, and comparing data

- Representing data

- Designing and carrying out a data investigation

Benchmarks

- Organize, represent, and describe categorical data, choosing categories that help make sense of the data.

- Interpret a bar graph.

- Make a line plot for a set of numerical data.

- Describe the shape of the data for a numerical data set, including where data are concentrated, where there are few data, what the lowest and highest values are, what the mode is, and where there is an outlier.

- Summarize a set of data, describing concentrations of data and what those concentrations mean in terms of the situation the data represent.

Geometry and Measurement

Students study the attributes of two-dimensional (2-D) and three-dimensional (3-D) shapes and how these attributes determine their classification. For example, a polygon is classified as a triangle or a quadrilateral based on the number of its sides.

triangles   *quadrilaterals*

Students also investigate the idea that one shape may have more than one name as they consider the properties of squares and rectangles. They describe shapes by whether or not they are congruent to other shapes and use geometric motions—slides (translations), flips (reflections), and turns (rotations)—to determine if two shapes are congruent.

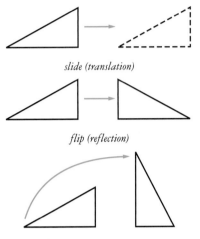

slide (translation)

flip (reflection)

turn (rotation)

Students describe attributes of common geometric solids (3-D shapes), such as how many edges and faces a solid shape has or how a pyramid has triangular faces coming to a point. They learn to distinguish between polyhedra (3-D shapes having only flat surfaces) and nonpolyhedra (3-D shapes that have curved surfaces) and, within the class of polyhedra, between prisms and pyramids.

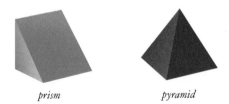

prism   *pyramid*

Students learn how 3-D objects can be represented in 2-D space. For example, they design nets for open boxes that, if constructed in 3-D, would hold a certain number of cubes. They determine the volume of rectangular prisms that fit into a variety of open boxes.

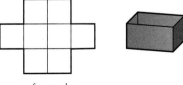

*net for open box
to hold two cubes*

Students' measurement work in grade 3 includes linear measurement, area, angle measurement, and volume. They measure length and calculate perimeter with both English units (inches, feet, and yards) and metric units (centimeters and meters). Their work focuses on using measurement tools accurately and understanding the relationship between measures when the same length is measured with different units.

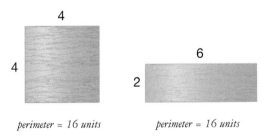

2 yards

6 feet

72 inches

Students learn that the distance around the outside edges of a 2-D shape is called the perimeter and consider how different shapes can have the same perimeter.

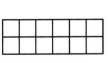

perimeter = 16 units   *perimeter = 16 units*

They identify the amount of 2-D space a given shape covers as its area and learn that area is measured in square units.

area = 16 square units   *area = 12 square units*

They identify the internal angle of a rectangle or square as 90 degrees. They use right angles as a benchmark as they consider the sizes of angles of other polygons.

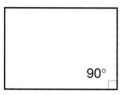

Mathematical Emphases

Features of Shape
- Describing and classifying 2-D figures

- Describing and measuring angles

- Describing properties of 3-D shapes

- Translating between 2-D and 3-D shapes

Linear Measurement
- Measuring length

- Measuring with standard units

- Understanding and finding perimeter

Area Measurement
- Understanding and finding area

Volume
- Structuring rectangular prisms and determining their volume

Benchmarks
- Identify and measure the perimeter of a figure using U.S. standard and metric units.

- Identify and find the area of given figures by counting whole and partial square units.

- Identify triangles as three-sided closed figures with three vertices and three angles.

- Identify right angles and recognize whether an angle is larger or smaller than a right angle.

- Identify and compare attributes of 3-D solids.

- Determine the number of cubes (volume) that will fit in the box made by a given pattern.

- Design patterns for boxes that will hold a given number of cubes.

PART 4

Ten-Minute Math and Classroom Routines

Curriculum Unit	1	2	3	4	5	6	7	8	9
Ten-Minute Math									
Counting Around the Class					●			●	
Guess My Rule		●				●		●	
More or Less?	●	●							●
Practicing Place Value	●			●					
Quick Images				●					●
Today's Number		●	●			●	●		
What Time Is It?			●		●		●		
Classroom Routines									
Class Collection			●						
What's the Temperature?	●	●	●	●	●	●	●	●	●

Preview

Ten-Minute Math activities and Classroom Routines offer practice and review of key concepts at each grade level. The two types of activities differ mainly in how and when they are integrated into your class day. Classroom Routines appear throughout Grades K–2, and two are included in Grade 3. These routines occur at regular intervals, perhaps during morning meeting, at the beginning of math class, or at another convenient time.

Ten-Minute Math activities appear throughout Grades 3–5. These short activities, designed to take no longer than 10 minutes, support and balance the in-depth work of each curriculum unit. After their first introduction in a math session, they are intended for use outside of math time. Some teachers use them to bring the whole class together just before or after lunch or recess or at the beginning or end of the day.

At Grade 3, seven Ten-Minute Math activities and two Classroom Routines are woven through the nine curriculum units. The following pages contain complete procedures for these activities, including the variations intended for use in Grade 3. Specific suggestions for use are found in Today's Plan for each session. It is recommended that you begin with the suggested daily problems and adapt them to fit the needs of your students throughout the year. Any needed preparation is noted in the Investigation Planner.

Ten Minute Math: Counting Around the Class

Students count around the class by a particular number, such as 2, 5, or 9. If students count by 2, the first student says "2," the next student says "4," the next "6," and so on. Before the count starts, students try to estimate the ending number of the count (the number the last person in the class will say). During and after the count, students discuss the relationships between the chosen factor and its multiples.

Math Focus Points

Students practice counting by different numbers and reasoning about relationships among factors and their multiples.

◆ Finding the multiples of numbers through skip counting

◆ Becoming familiar with multiplication patterns

◆ Understanding the relationship between skip counting and multiplication

Counting Around the Class is introduced in Session 1.3 in Unit 5, *Equal Groups;* it also appears in Unit 8, *How Many Hundreds? How Many Miles?*

Basic Activity

Step 1 Choose a number to count by. For example, if the class has been working with quarters recently, you might want to count by 25.

Step 2 Ask students to estimate the target number.

If we count around the class by 25, what number will the last person in the class say?

Encourage students to talk about how they could determine the last number without actually counting.

Step 3 Count around the class by your chosen number. Students count: "25, . . . 50, . . . 75, ..." If some students seem uncertain about what number comes next, consider

writing the numbers on the board as students say them. Seeing visual patterns often helps students with the spoken pattern.

You might also count around a second time by the same number, starting with a different person, so that students hear the same pattern more than once and have their turns at different points in the sequence.

Step 4 Pause in the middle of the count to look back. To help students think about the relationship between a factor and its multiples, ask questions such as the following:

We're up to 375, counting by 25. How many students have counted so far? How do you know?

Step 5 Extend the problem. Ask questions like the following:

Which of your estimations were reasonable? Which were possible? Which were impossible? (A student might remark, for example, "You can't have 510 for 25s because 25 lands only on the 25s, the 50s, the 75s, and the 100s.")

What if we had 32 students in this class instead of 28? What would the ending number be?

What if we counted by a different number? This time we counted by 25 and ended on 700. What if we counted by 50? What do you think would be the ending number? Why do you think it would be twice as big? How did you figure that out?

Teaching Notes

Let Students Prepare

Whenever you introduce an unfamiliar number to count by, some students may need some preparation before they begin counting around the class. Ask students to work in pairs, with whatever materials they want, to determine the ending for the count.

Avoid Competition

Be sensitive to the possibility that some students may be embarrassed or feel "put on the spot" because of the structure of the activity. Some teachers allow students to volunteer for the next number, rather than counting in a particular order. Other teachers make the count a cooperative effort, establishing an atmosphere in which students readily help each other, where anyone feels free to ask for help.

Variations

What Could We Count By?

Specify a target number, such as 24, 25, 50, 72, 100, or 1,000. Ask:

What number (or numbers) could we count by so someone in our class would land on (25)?

Encourage students to share their strategies for figuring this out. Count around the class by the suggested numbers to see if they work.

Counting Backward

Starting with a given number, count backward around the class. Choose numbers with patterns that are already familiar to students. For example, start at 400 and count backward by 2, 5, 10, or 25.

Alternatively, play a modified version of *What Could We Count By?* Give students a starting number (such as 100 or 1,000) and ask them to find a number they could count by, backward, that would land exactly on 0 (or so that someone would say a particular number during the count).

Ten-Minute Math: Guess My Rule

In this classification game, students decide, through careful observation and questioning, what characteristics a group of people or things has in common. The leader secretly establishes a "rule," for example, HAS BROWN HAIR (describing a portion of the class) or EVERGREEN (describing certain kinds of trees). The leader then identifies specific people or items that fit or do not fit the rule. Students use this evidence to make guesses to deduce the rule.

Math Focus Points

Guess My Rule involves students in logical reasoning about the common characteristics or properties of people or things that follow a given rule. In the number variation, students investigate aspects of number theory.

◆ Using evidence and formulating questions to make hypotheses about the common characteristics in groups of things

◆ Systematically eliminating possibilities

◆ Using mathematical terms to describe numbers

Guess My Rule is introduced in Session 1.3 in Unit 2, *Surveys and Line Plots;* it also appears in Unit 6, *Stories, Tables, and Graphs;* and in Unit 8, *How Many Hundreds? How Many Miles?*

Materials

• Chart paper (optional)

Basic Activity

Step 1 Choose a rule. Choose a visually obvious rule that describes some students in the classroom, such as HAS BROWN HAIR, WEARING RED, or WEARING A WATCH. Choose two students who fit the rule, without revealing what the rule is, and ask these students to stand where other students can clearly see them.

Step 2 Students work to discover your rule. Emphasize that no one is to guess the rule out loud. After observing the two students who fit the rule and silently considering what the rule might be, students test their hypotheses by naming other students who they think also fit the rule. If the student named does fit the rule, ask him or her to stand with the others who fit the rule. If the student named does not fit the rule, ask him or her to stand in a different place in the room. Students can then observe both groups and use this information to eliminate possibilities, devise new solutions, and revise their ideas of what the rule might be.

Step 3 Record students' suggestions for what the rule might be. When many students seem to have a good idea about what the rule is, list all their proposed rules on the board or on chart paper. Students may challenge any rules that they think don't fit all the clues, giving reasons for their challenges.

Step 4 Invite students to ask further questions. If more than one suggested rule still fits all the clues, students should continue to offer examples until only one rule remains. Encourage students to ask questions that eliminate more than one of the proposed rules.

Step 5 Ask what fraction fits the rule. (This step is to be included after students have studied fractions.) Once students guess your rule, ask them to figure out what fraction of the class fits the rule and what fraction does not and to also find familiar fractions for the numbers they discover. For example,

Eight out of 21 students wore red today. What fraction is that? $\left(\frac{8}{21}\right)$ What familiar fraction is that close to? $\left(\frac{1}{3}\right)$ Is it a little more than one third of the class or a little less than one third?

Variations

Guess My Rule with Things

Choose a rule that describes certain kinds of things, such as plants, animals, places, or objects. For example, instead of just TREES, your rule might be EVERGREEN TREES. Or your rule might be THINGS THAT HAVE WHEELS or ANIMALS WITH FOUR LEGS. Draw a circle on the board and explain that every word you place *inside* the circle names something that fits your rule. If you place a word outside the circle, that thing does *not* fit your rule. Begin by placing a few examples inside the circle and one or two outside the circle.

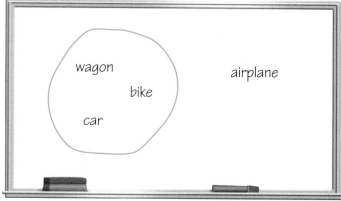

Example: Things that move on the ground

Guess My Rule with Numbers

Choose a rule that describes a number characteristic, such as factor, multiple, odd, even, square, or prime. For example, your rule might be MULTIPLES OF 5, FACTORS OF 48, or NUMBERS GREATER THAN 100. Draw a circle on the board and explain that every number you place inside the circle fits your rule. If you place a number outside the circle, that number does *not* fit your rule. Begin by placing a few examples inside the circle and one or two outside the circle.

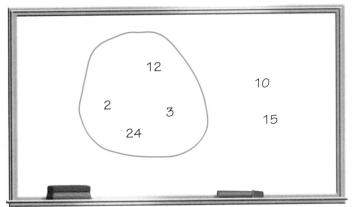

Example: Factors of 24

Ten-Minute Math: More or Less?

Students use estimation to determine whether the sum or difference of an arithmetic problem they see displayed for a brief time is "more or less than 100" or "more or less than $1.00." They share their strategies for making their decisions.

Math Focus Points

Students develop strategies for mental computation and judge the reasonableness of solutions found using either paper and pencil calculations or a calculator.

◆ Breaking apart, reordering, or combining numbers within a problem for easier computation

◆ Using knowledge of place value and known combinations to estimate sums and differences

◆ Practicing addition and subtraction skills

More or Less? is introduced in Session 2.3 in Unit 1, *Trading Stickers, Combining Coins;* it also appears in Unit 2, *Surveys and Line Plots;* and in Unit 9, *Solids and Boxes.*

Materials

• Chart paper or overhead projector

Basic Activity

Step 1 Present a problem. Write a problem on the overhead or at the top of chart paper; for example: 55 + 38. Begin with problems that contain two to four one- and two-digit addends; then gradually move toward including subtraction, both addition and subtraction, and numbers in the hundreds.

Step 2 Ask, "Is it more or less than 100?" Ask students to answer this question by estimating the answer to the problem. Allow between 15 and 30 seconds for students to think about the problem. Set a time limit based on the complexity of the problem. Students come up with the best estimate they can, without pencil and paper or using a calculator. This estimate may be, but will not usually be, the exact answer.

Step 3 **Students share strategies.** Ask questions like the following:

What did you pay attention to when you looked at the number in this problem? How did you know that the estimate was more than (less than) 100 ($1.00)? Did you use landmark numbers or combinations you know that equal 100 or $1.00 to help you figure it out?

For example, given the problem $44 + 30 + 37$, one student might reason:

"I looked at the tens in the first two numbers. I know that 40 + 30 equals 70. I know that 70 + 30 equals 100. Since the last number is 37, the answer has to be more than 100."

(Optional) **Step 4** **Compare estimates to exact answer.** If some students have mentally determined the exact answer (and if time allows), you can ask those students to share the exact answer and their strategies for figuring it out. (Alternatively, you can ask students to use a calculator to determine the correct answer.) Then ask:

How far from the exact answer was your estimate? Are there strategies that you heard from your classmates that can help you develop better estimation skills?

Ten-Minute Math: Practicing Place Value

Students practice reading and writing numbers up to 1,000. Then students add 10 and multiples of 10 or subtract 10 and multiples of 10 from the given numbers. Students discuss how the values of the digits change in each equation. Students develop flexibility in decomposing numbers as they break three-digit numbers into hundreds, tens, and ones in various ways and demonstrate their equivalence.

Math Focus Points

Students focus on how numbers are composed and how written numerals relate to the quantity they represent.

◈ Recognizing and interpreting the value of each digit in two- and three-digit numbers

◈ Finding different combinations of a number, using only 100s, 10s, and 1s, and recognizing their equivalence (e.g., 1 hundred, 3 tens, and 7 ones = 1 hundred, 2 tens, and 17 ones = 13 tens and 7 ones = 12 tens and 17 ones; etc.)

◈ Reading and writing numbers up to 1,000

◈ Adding multiples of 10 to and subtracting them from two- and three-digit numbers

Practicing Place Value is introduced in Session 1.1 in Unit 1, *Trading Stickers, Combining Coins;* it also appears in Unit 4, *Perimeter, Angles, and Area;* and in Unit 9, *Solids and Boxes.*

Materials

- Blank paper and pencil

- Cubes, organized in towers of ten (10 towers per pair)

- Overhead projector

- Transparency T1, *Practicing Place Value*

- Transparencies T2, *Stickers: Strips and Singles* (cut apart)

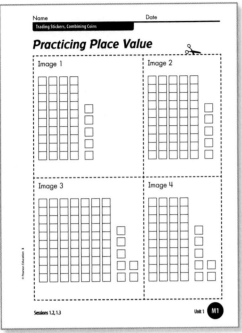

▲ Resource Masters, Unit 1 M1; Transparencies, T1

▲ Resource Masters, Unit 1 M2; Transparencies, T2

Basic Activity

Step 1 Write or say a number. Your choice of number will depend on the size of the numbers your students are working on or need work with. Alternate between writing the numbers on the board and reading them aloud. For example, write 135 or say "one hundred, thirty-five."

Step 2 Students say or write the number. Give all students an opportunity to read, write, and say this number correctly. Ask a volunteer to say or write the number for the whole class.

Step 3 Add or subtract multiples of 10. Write or say a series of addition and/or subtraction problems, adding or subtracting multiples of 10 (tens or hundreds) to the starting number. For example,

What is 135 + 20? 135 + 40? 135 + 60? 135 + 200? 135 + 400? 135 + 600?

or

What is 135 + 20? 135 − 20? 135 + 30? 135 − 30? 135 + 100? 135 − 100?

Step 4 Students mentally solve the problems. After students solve the problems mentally and share their solutions with a partner, ask a few volunteers to share their solutions with the class. As students share their solutions, record the equations (e.g., 135 + 20 = 155, 135 − 100 = 35) on the board.

Step 5 Discuss place value. Ask students to compare each sum or difference with the starting number (for example, for the problem 135 + 20, compare 155 and 135). Ask:

Which places in the two numbers have the same digits? Which do not? Why? Did the number get bigger or smaller? By how much?

Step 6 If time remains, pose additional similar problems.

Variations

Stickers and Cubes

Step 1 Show a number in strips and singles. Show a two-digit number on the overhead, using transparent stickers in strips of ten and singles or using towers of ten cubes and single cubes. Let students see the image for 5–8 seconds, depending on the size of the number. Then cover the image. Have students write the number and then build it with cubes.

Step 2 Show the number in strips and singles again. Show the sticker strips and singles (or cubes) again and let students adjust what they built. Ask:

What number does the image represent? How do you know? How many towers of ten and single cubes did you use to build it? How many stickers will there be if I add 1 (or 2, 3, 4, . . .) more strips of ten to the image?

or

How many stickers will there be if I subtract 1 (or 2, 3, 4, . . .) strips of ten from this image?

Step 3 Students write and build the new number. Have students write the new number and build it with cubes. Ask:

What number does the image represent now? How do you know? How many towers of ten and single cubes did you use to build it?

You may also begin by *writing* the number instead of showing strips and singles. Have students use cubes to build the number; then follow the previous procedure.

As students become proficient with larger numbers, show images that include sheets of 100 and ask students to add or subtract larger multiples of 10 and 100. Students will not build the larger numbers with cubes, but they can sketch the number shown and the new numbers with the agreed-on shorthand method (e.g., large squares, lines, and dots).

How Many Tens?

In this variation, students decompose numbers by place. Doing so involves more than just naming the number in each place. It includes understanding, for example, that while 435 is composed of 4 hundreds, 3 tens, and 5 ones, it can also be broken up into 3 hundreds, 13 tens, and 5 ones; or 2 hundreds, 23 tens, and 5 ones; or 1 hundred, 33 tens, and 5 ones; or 43 tens and 5 ones.

Step 1 Write or say a number. Write a number on the board (or say it and have students write it). For example:

135

Step 2 Ask: "How many groups of ten are in the number? How many ones would be left?" For example, ask students how many groups of ten can be made from 135 items.

If we had towers of ten cubes or strips of ten stickers, how many towers or strips would there be to make this number?

Establish with students that there are 13 tens and 5 ones in this number.

Step 3 Pose additional questions. Pose a series of related questions, such as the following:

If I wanted to break up 135 so that there were some tens and *15* ones, how many tens would there be? (12 tens) What if I wanted *25* ones? (11 tens)

What if I wanted 10 tens? How many ones would there be? (35 ones)

What if I wanted 8 tens? How many ones would there be? (55 ones)

Once students understand the intent of this activity, use larger numbers (e.g., how many tens are there in 283 or 349?). You can also ask them to write five combinations for the given number, using the places you specify. (For example, for the number 283, they could write five combinations that equal 283: 28 tens and 3 ones, 27 tens and 13 ones, 26 tens and 23 ones, and so on.)

Ten-Minute Math: Quick Images

In this activity, students visualize and analyze images of geometric figures. After briefly viewing an image of a 2-dimensional (2-D) design or 3-dimensional (3-D) structure, students either draw it or build it from the mental image they formed during the brief viewing. They might see it as a whole ("it looks like a box, three cubes long and two cubes high") or decompose it into memorable parts ("it looks like four triangles—right side up, then upside down, then right side up, then upside down").

Math Focus Points

Students visualize and reconstruct geometric images (of 2-D geometric designs or 3-D cube structures), either as a whole or by decomposing them into memorable parts.

◆ Organizing and analyzing visual images

◆ Developing language and concepts needed to communicate about spatial relationships

Quick Images is introduced in Session 1.5 in Unit 4, *Perimeter, Angles, and Area;* it also appears in Unit 9, *Solids and Boxes.*

Materials

• Overhead projector

• Transparencies T104–T106, *Quick Images*

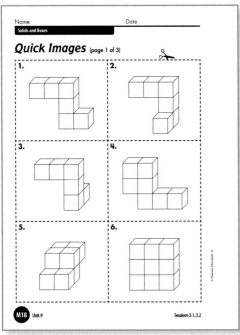

Name _____ **Date** _____

Solids and Boxes

Quick Images (page 1 of 3)

1.
2.
3.
4.
5.
6.

M18 Unit 9   Sessions 3.1, 3.2

▲ **Resource Masters, Unit 9 M18; Transparencies, T104**

Basic Activity

Step 1 Flash an image for 3 seconds. It is important to show the figure for as close to 3 seconds as possible. If you show it too long, students will draw or build from the figure rather than from their mental image of it; if you show it too briefly, they will not have sufficient time to form a mental image. Students quickly learn to study the figure carefully while it is visible so they can draw or build it from their mental image.

Step 2 Students draw or build what they saw. Give students a few minutes with the relevant materials (paper and pencil, cubes) to draw or construct a figure that matches the mental image they formed. When you see that most students have finished working, proceed to step 3.

Step 3 Flash the image again for 3 seconds, this time for revision. After showing the same image for another 3 seconds, students revise their drawings or structures according to what they see in this second viewing. It is essential to provide enough time here, before a third showing, for most students to complete their attempts at drawing or building. While they may not have completed their figures, they should have done all they can until they see the image displayed again. When student work subsides, proceed to step 4.

Step 4 Show the image a third and final time. This time leave the image visible so that all students can complete or revise their drawings or structures.

Step 5 Discuss the mental images students formed. Students explain the different ways they saw the figure as they looked at it on successive "flashes." Encourage students to explain what relationships they used in decomposing the figure.

Variations

Quick Images: 2-D

Quick Images: 2-D is introduced in Session 1.5 in Unit 4, *Perimeter, Angles, and Area.*

Materials

- Transparencies T52–T54, *Quick Images: 2-D*

- Blank paper and pencil

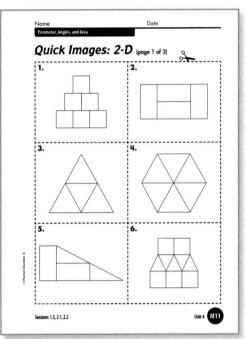

▲ Resource Masters, Unit 4 M11; Transparencies, T52

Math Focus Point

◆ Decomposing images of 2-D shapes and then recombining them to make a given design

Following the procedure for the basic activity, students will use paper and pencil to draw the 2-D designs they see.

Teaching Note *Helping Students Organize the Images* When talking about what they saw in successive flashes, many students will say things like "I saw four triangles in a row." For students having difficulty, suggest the following:

Each design is made from familiar geometric shapes. Find these shapes and try to figure out how they are put together.

As students describe their figures, you can introduce the correct geometric terms for component shapes. As you use these terms naturally in class discussion, students will begin to recognize and use them more frequently and accurately.

Quick Images: 3-D

Quick Images: 3-D is introduced in Session 3.1 in Unit 9, *Solids and Boxes*.

Materials

- Transparencies T104–T106, *Quick Images: 3-D*

- Connecting cubes (15–20 per student)

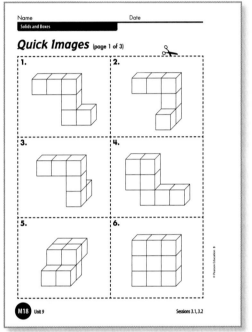

▲ Resource Masters, Unit 4 M18; Transparencies, T104

Math Focus Point

◆ Decomposing images of 3-D shapes and then recombining them to make a given structure

For this version, students follow the procedure in the basic activity but build images of the cube buildings they see. Each student will need 15–20 connecting cubes. Several of the cube figures on the transparencies are intentionally ambiguous, as some unseen cubes "in the back" may or may not be a part of the figure. Students with differing solutions should have an opportunity to compare and defend their constructions.

Ten-Minute Math: Today's Number

Students write several different expressions that equal a given number. They do so in the context of constraints that define the operations and number relationships they can use. Constraints on what numbers or operations students can use encourage students to be flexible in their use of arithmetic skills and provide a focus on the particular number or computation work that students need to develop or practice.

Math Focus Points

Today's Number provides computation practice and an opportunity for students to demonstrate flexibility in a variety of expressions that equal a given number.

◈ Generating equivalent expressions for a number using particular constraints

◈ Practicing computation skills

◈ Using notation to record expressions

Today's Number is introduced in Session 1.6 in Unit 2, *Surveys and Line Plots;* it also appears in Unit 3, *Collections and Travel Stories;* in Unit 6, *Stories, Tables, and Graphs;* and in Unit 7, *Finding Fair Shares.*

Materials

• Blank paper and pencil

• Chart paper and markers

Basic Activity

Step 1 Record today's number. Write the number chosen for the day at the top of the chart paper.

Step 2 Define and record the constraint(s). Define the constraints and record them on the chart paper. Using constraints—such as limiting students to particular operations, requiring them to use certain kinds of numbers, or specifying how they should compose or decompose the numbers in their expressions—provides an opportunity to reinforce the work students have been doing in this and previous number units.

For example, here are some constraints that offer students addition and subtraction practice throughout Grade 3:

• Use one or more multiples of ten.

• Use subtraction only.

• Use both addition and subtraction in each equation.

• Use at least one three-digit number.

• Use one or more combinations that add to 100.

• Use at least two operations and start with a number greater than 100.

Step 3 Students write expressions. Give students a few minutes to write expressions that equal today's number.

Step 4 List the expressions that students suggest. Use the chart paper to list students' expressions. As you do so, invite the rest of the class to confirm each suggestion or to discuss any incorrect responses and explain their thinking.

Watch for examples that offer opportunities to engage students in brief discussions about some of the larger ideas about number that they encounter in Grade 3. For example, two students may have created expressions that contain the same numbers in a different sequence. This provides a good context for asking, "Does the order matter?"

Teaching Note

Use of Parentheses

Students often write expressions that contain more than one operation. Explain to students that there are rules about solving equations with more than one operation and that parentheses are used to indicate which part of the problem should be solved first. Using the order of operations, $4 + 3 \times 5 = 19$ because multiplication is solved before addition. Show students how using parentheses in different parts of the equation can result in a different answer: for example, $4 + (3 \times 5) = 19$ but $(4 + 3) \times 5 = 35$.

Variations

Looking for Patterns

Encourage students to find expressions that they can alter systematically to find more expressions. For example, here is a pattern that a student devised for 100.

2×50

$2 \times 49 + 2$

$2 \times 48 + 4$

$2 \times 47 + 6$

$2 \times 46 + 8$

Working Backward

Write expressions for today's number and ask students to determine what number you are expressing. For example, if today's number is 225, you could write $(20 \times 5) + (400 \div 2) - 75$ and $(50 \times 4) + (100 \div 2) - 25$.

When students are finished, ask,

How many operations are in each expression? Which operations appear in each expression? How did you solve each problem?

If time allows, ask students to create their own expressions equaling today's number.

Ten-Minute Math: What Time Is It?

Students practice naming, notating, and telling time to the minute on digital and analog clocks. They predict ending times when given intervals and the starting times of activities. Conversely, they predict starting times when given intervals and the ending times. They also determine intervals when given both the starting and ending times.

Math Focus Points

Students practice telling time, predict what time it will be, and determine the length of various amounts of time.

◆ Naming, notating, and telling time to the nearest 5 minutes on a digital or analog clock

◆ Telling time to any minute on a digital or analog clock

◆ Determining intervals of time to the minute

What Time Is It? is introduced in Session 3.1 in Unit 3, *Collections and Travel Stories;* it also appears in Unit 5, *Equal Groups;* and in Unit 7, *Finding Fair Shares.*

Materials

• Large demonstration analog clock

• Student analog clocks (one per pair)

Basic Activity

Step 1 **Write or display the time.** Write a time at an interval of 5 minutes (for example, 12:05 or 12:35) on the board or show the time on the demonstration clock. Ask students to say the time and to set that time on their clocks. Alternatively, you may say the time and ask students to write it before setting it on their clocks.

Step 2 **Write or display a change in time.** Move the minute hand on the demonstration clock to the next 5-minute interval. Move the hour hand slightly as well (for example, slightly past the 12 when beginning with the time 12:05), again asking students to tell what time it is.

Step 3 **Record the new time on the board.** Ask:

If I move the minute hand to the 3, what time will it be? What about the 4? What time will it be then? What about the 5?

Continue to record the times on the board and identify each new time. Check for students' understanding of the different ways to name each time you record. For example,

Sometimes people call this time 12:25. What else do people call this time? (25 minutes after 12) Sometimes people call this time 12:50. What's another way to say this time? (10 minutes before 1)

Step 4 **Students demonstrate 5-minute intervals.** Working in pairs, students practice setting their clocks to 5-minute intervals that you suggest (for example, 1:10, 1:15, 1:20, . . ., 1:45, 1:50, 1:55).

Variations

Telling Time to the Minute

Follow the procedure for the basic activity but use any time, including times in between 5-minute intervals (e.g., 3:12 or 3:38). Check that students can say what time it is (for example, that 3:12 is 12 minutes past 3 o'clock or that 3:38 can also be read as 38 past 3 or 22 minutes before 4 o'clock). Do they know what interval of 5 minutes the times fall between (3:10 and 3:15; 3:35 and 3:40)?

What Time Is It? What Time Will it Be?

In this variation, students begin with a time and determine what the time will be after a given number of minutes have passed.

For example, write a time on the board (or say the time) or show a time on the demonstration clock. Alternate using times at 5-minute intervals and times in between 5-minute intervals. Ask students to set that time on their clocks. Begin by asking questions like the following:

What time is it? What time will it be in one hour (one-half hour, 15 minutes, etc.)?

Students set their clocks and discuss how they determined the time and how the hands moved on the clock. Record the new time on the board and repeat as above.

or

Have students determine the duration of daily activities. Show a time on the demonstration clock and ask,

What time is it?

Then ask questions like the following:

If Writing Workshop starts at 9:10 and lasts for 45 minutes, what time will it end? If you start reading tonight at 6:45 and read silently for 30 minutes, what time will it be when you're done?

Allow students to share ideas with a partner about what time they think it will be.

How Long Did It Take?

In this variation, students are given a starting and ending time and asked to determine the interval or how much time has passed.

Tell students a story like the following:

I visited my friend on Saturday. I got to her house at 10:30 and stayed there until 11:45. How long did I visit my friend?

Allow students to talk to a partner and share ideas. As a class, make sure students can visualize this new situation of finding the interval instead of finding the ending time. Collect ideas and focus on strategies in which students count the interval in chunks (such as 60 minutes from 10:30 to 11:30 plus 15 minutes more to 11:45 is 75 minutes, or 1 hour and 15 minutes total).

Classroom Routine: Class Collection

Students select an item to collect as a class. Students collect 1,000 of that item and keep track of the class collection as it grows.

Math Focus Points

Students practice addition and subtraction and further their understanding of the structure of 1,000 as they collect, calculate, and represent 1,000 items.

◆ Solving addition problems with two-and three-digit numbers

◆ Finding the difference between three-digit numbers

◆ Finding the difference between two- and three-digit numbers and 1,000

Class Collection is introduced in Session 1.4 in Unit 3, *Collections and Travel Stories*; it appears in that unit only.

Materials

• Class 1,000 chart (second copy prepared ahead of time for *Class Collection*)

• Unit 3 Resource Masters M27–M28, Class Collection Data Chart (one copy for each week of the class collection)

• Dot stickers (optional) or markers

Activity

This routine is done twice a week outside of math class until the collection is complete. The Class Collection Data Chart sets Wednesday and Friday as the two days for this routine, although you may adjust this timing to fit the particular schedule of your classroom.

The routine is carried out as follows:

Step 1 Choose a goal for the week. The class chooses a goal for the week's collection, for example, to collect 250 items. The goal is recorded on the Class Collection Data Chart.

▲ Resource Masters, Unit 3 M27–M28

Step 2 Record quantities on the Class Collection Data Chart each day. Each student records on the Class Collection Data Chart the quantity of items that he or she has brought in. This is done each day when the student arrives in the classroom.

Step 3 Determine the midweek total. On Wednesday, students figure out the individual totals for Monday, Tuesday, and Wednesday. After doing so they determine the three-day total. Students then determine how far the three-day total is from the week's goal; in other words, how many more do they need to collect on Thursday and Friday to reach the goal?

Step 4 Determine the weekly total. On Friday, students figure out the two-day total, the total for the week, the total amount of items in the collection so far, and how many more they will need to collect to reach 1,000.

Step 5 Represent the total on the class 1,000 chart. The week's total is represented on the class 1,000 chart by filling in that number of squares. This gives students a visual representation of the collection's growth and the distance from 1,000.

Teaching Note

Varying This Routine

You can decide exactly how to carry out the routine to fit your class schedule. For example, you can

- share strategies for some of these calculations in a whole-group discussion.

- assign the daily total as homework.

- assign the daily total as work for the students to do as they come into the classroom. (Students may work on the total from the day before.)

Classroom Routine: What's the Temperature?

Students learn how to read a thermometer and learn what different temperatures feel like (using both Fahrenheit and Celsius scales). In addition, students become familiar with charts and graphs and the relationships between them.

Math Focus Points

Students record the outside temperature on a chart and a graph and describe changes in temperature over time.

◆ Learning about temperature: reading a thermometer, learning to associate different temperatures with words like *colder* and *warmer,* and establishing landmark temperatures

◆ Recording information in a table and on a graph

◆ Reading information from the shape of a graph, for example, hot, cold, increasing, decreasing

What's the Temperature? is introduced in Session 1.1 in Unit 1, *Trading Stickers, Combining Coins.* You will do it once each week on Wednesday morning throughout the school year.

What's the Temperature? lays the groundwork for Investigation 1 in Unit 6, *Stories, Tables, and Graphs,* which begins by looking at the temperature information recorded in the chart and graph since the beginning of the school year. Therefore, it is important to collect the data every week from the beginning of the year.

Materials

● A thermometer mounted outside so it can be read from a classroom window

● A wall chart with columns labeled Date and Temperature. If you are using a Celsius/Fahrenheit thermometer, then there should be three columns: Date, Temperature (°C), and Temperature (°F). Rows should be labeled by the dates of each Wednesday of the school year. Include vacation weeks.

● A wall graph with vertical axis labeled Temperature: Fahrenheit and the scale extending from 10 to 100 degrees. (If temperatures in your area are likely to read below 10 or over 100, extend your scale to include those temperatures.) The horizontal axis, labeled Date, should indicate each Wednesday of the school year. You might design the graph with different colored paper as background to indicate temperature ranges: red for hot temperatures; yellow for warm temperatures; green for cool temperatures; blue for cold temperatures.

● Black and white sticker dots (or any other 2 clearly visible colors)

Procedure for Weekly Recording of Temperature

Step 1 Student reads and reports the temperature. Each Wednesday morning, a student reads the thermometer and reports the temperature to the class.

Step 2 Record the temperature on the chart and the graph. First record the temperature on the wall chart. Then, on the wall graph, place a black dot above the date on the point that indicates the temperature reading.

Here is an example of a chart and graph with the first three weekly readings filled in:

Date	Temperature (°F)	Temperature (°C)
September 8	72	22
September 15	74	23
September 22	61	16
September 29		
October 6		

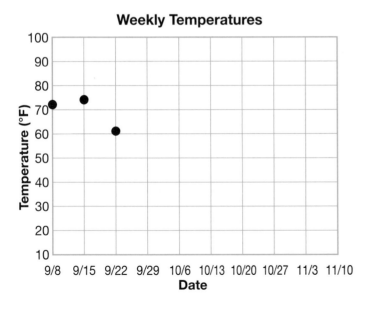

Weekly Temperatures

This routine will take place throughout the entire year. We recommend that you make recordings once each week so that the table and graph don't become too large. However, to give students more practice in plotting points on a graph, you might choose to have one student read the temperature every morning and have another student point to where that reading would appear on the graph.

Step 3 Discuss what students notice. Students may notice that their readings are not exactly the same as the temperatures they hear on the news or see in displays on buildings in town. This provides an opportunity to discuss how temperatures change during the day. Also, the temperature outside the class window might not be exactly the same as the temperature in another nearby location.

Procedure for Monthly Discussions

Step 1 Look at the graph and discuss the temperature data collected so far. Approximately once each month, look at the graph and discuss the temperature data collected so far in the year. Ask questions like the following:

What is the temperature now and how does it feel? What kind of clothes are you wearing outside now? What kind of outdoor activities can you do?

Over the last month has it been warm or cold? Have the temperatures increased, decreased, or stayed the same? How can you tell that from the graph?

Where on the graph do you see the most change? Did it change suddenly or gradually?

Step 2 Make predictions about the temperature range for the coming month. Have the class predict what temperature range they can expect for the coming month. Ask questions like the following:

Will it be colder or warmer or stay the same? If you expect the temperatures to change, what kind of clothing do you think you'll be wearing outside? What kinds of activities will you enjoy doing outside?

Place white stickers to indicate the temperature ranges they expect for the next four Wednesdays.

Step 3 Compare the actual temperatures to the previous month's predictions. When you have this discussion the following month, students will compare the actual temperatures to their predictions. Ask:

Was it colder or warmer than you predicted? Did the changes occur when you thought they would?

Remove the previous month's predictions before making predictions for the coming month.

Additional Discussion Options

Shape of the Line

After about three months, discuss with students the wiggliness of the line versus the overall shape. In most locations in the United States, temperatures will tend to go down from the beginning of school into the months of autumn. But from one week to the next, the temperature might go up or down.

After a Vacation

After a vacation week, you will have blanks in the chart and the graph. Ask the class to look at the temperature the week before vacation and the week after. What do they think the temperature was likely to have been on the Wednesday of vacation? Do they remember if it was unusually warm, unusually cold, or pretty much the same as usual?

If your students visited different places during a vacation week, ask them about the temperatures where they were. Was it warmer or colder than home? What clothing did they wear?

Temperatures in Other Places

If your students have lived in different places, ask them to talk about the temperatures where they lived. If they have friends or relatives who live in different places, you might suggest that they ask their friends or relatives what the temperatures are like there. Students can report what they learn to the class. You can also point to these places on a map.

PART 5

Technology in *Investigations*

Preview

The *Investigations* curriculum incorporates two forms of technology: calculators and computers. Calculators are assumed to be standard mathematical tools, available for student use as appropriate. Computers, on the other hand, are explicitly linked to one or more curriculum units at each grade level through software that is provided with the curriculum.

Using Calculators with the Curriculum

Students should become comfortable using a basic calculator as a tool that is common in their homes and communities. Increasingly sophisticated calculators are being developed and used in settings ranging from high school mathematics courses to science, business, and construction. Students need to learn how to use the calculator effectively and appropriately as a tool, just as they need to learn to read a clock, interpret a map, measure with a ruler, or use coins. They should use calculators for sensible purposes—just as you would do—not as a replacement for mental calculations or for pencil and paper calculations they are learning to do. Encourage students to use calculators to double-check calculations, as an aid if they have many calculations to carry out outside of math class, or to solve problems for which they can think out a solution but don't yet have the experience to carry out the computation.

Calculators are recommended for a few specific activities in curriculum units. For most of the work on number and operations, students are using their own representations and reasoning to solve problems as they develop computational fluency. Calculators might sometimes be used for double-checking, although students should also be able to double-check their work without a calculator.

Look for situations in the classroom when the purpose of the mathematical activity is not the development of computational fluency and when the numbers and calculations are beyond the students' skills in written or mental computation. These situations provide opportunities for students to practice estimating reasonable results and then carrying out the calculation with a calculator.

For example, students could work to find the total of a class book order. Pose some questions to help them estimate first:

Will the total be over $50? between $50 and $100? between $100 and $150?

Help them to think about grouping the books to estimate:

How many of the books cost close to $1.00 each?

Then students can carry out the complete calculation with a calculator.

Ask questions to help students learn good practices with the calculator:

How are you keeping track of which books you have added and which you still need to add?

Is your result reasonable according to your estimate?

How can you double-check the calculator result (for example, by subtracting off each book)?

Students enjoy using what they perceive as an adult tool. Investigating with the calculator gives students an opportunity to notice mathematical patterns and to ask questions about mathematical symbols. For example, in a second-grade class, students were dividing lots of numbers by 2, which led to a discussion of the meaning of 0.5. In a fourth-grade class, some students became intrigued with the square root sign. The teacher challenged them to systematically keep track of the results of applying the square root symbol to whole numbers, starting with 1, and to come up with an idea about its meaning.

The calculator is an efficient tool for many purposes in life, and students should learn to use it sensibly, knowing that using it well depends on the user's correct analysis and organization of the problem, comparing its results with reasonable estimates, and double-checking.

Introducing and Managing the *LogoPaths* Software in Grade 3

LogoPaths Software is provided as a component of the *Investigations* curriculum. While using this software is optional, we recommend its use if you have computers either in your classroom or in your school's computer lab. The *Software Support Reference Guide* provides a complete description of the software and instructions for using the software activities.

The *LogoPaths* Software is formally introduced in Grade 3, Unit 4, *Perimeter, Angles, and Area.* However, if you can give students some experience with the software early in the year, *before* Unit 4, they will be better prepared to use it to solve the specific problems in that unit.

Therefore, we recommend that you start using the software outside of math time starting with Unit 2, *Surveys and Line Plots,* by introducing *Get the Toys*—a game with basic commands involving forward and backward steps in multiples of 10 and turns of 90°. (Suggestions for introducing this game and the other software activities follow on page 44.)

In Unit 4, you will find suggestions for introducing the *LogoPaths* games and activities during specific sessions and integrating them into your Math Workshops. The software activities extend and deepen the mathematical ideas that are emphasized in this curriculum unit. In some cases, they allow students to work with geometric figures and with angles in ways that are not possible in the noncomputer activities.

Options for Introducing the *LogoPaths* Software

- *Computer lab:* If you have a computer laboratory with one computer for each pair of students, the entire class can become familiar with the computer activities at the same time. In this case, you will not need to devote time during math class to introduce the new software activity. Once an activity has been introduced, students can do it either during Math Workshop (if you have classroom computers) or during their scheduled lab time.

- *Large projection screen:* If you have a large projection screen, you can introduce the software activities to the whole class during a math session, immediately before Math Workshop or at another time of the day.

- *Small groups of students:* With fewer classroom computers, you can introduce the activities to small groups either before or during Math Workshop. These students can then be paired and become peer "teachers" of the software.

Regardless of the number of computers available, students generally benefit from working on these activities in pairs. This not only maximizes computer resources but also encourages students to consult, monitor, and teach one another. Generally, more than two students at one computer find it difficult to share. You may need to monitor computer use more closely than the other Math Workshop choices to ensure that all students get sufficient computer time. Each pair should spend at least 15–20 minutes at the computer for each activity.

Managing the Computer Environment

Students should be using the *LogoPaths* Software consistently throughout Unit 4 and periodically the rest of the school year. If you have daily access to a computer lab, you might take advantage of this to supplement your regular math class. If your school has a computer teacher, you might collaborate with that teacher to have students work on *LogoPaths* activities during some of their scheduled lab time.

More typically, a classroom will have a small number of computers. With computers in the classroom, pairs of students can cycle through the software activities during Math Workshop, just as they cycle through the other choices. Three to five classroom computers is ideal, but even with only one or two, students can have a successful computer experience. When you have fewer computers, find additional computer time for students throughout the day, outside of math.

Using *LogoPaths* All Year

After the formal introduction of the software in Unit 4, subsequent units each include a Technology Note with suggestions and reminders for ongoing use of the software during the rest of the year. Continued experience with *LogoPaths* allows students to become increasingly fluent in the mechanics of the software itself and able to better focus on the mathematical ideas of the game and activities.

Throughout Grade 3, the Resource Masters include some designed for continued student work with activities such as *Missing Measures* and *200 (400, 500) Steps*. Students should also continue to play the games *Get the Toys* and *Feed the Turtle*, which help develop an understanding of paths and turning angles. The *Free Explore* activities offer experiences with the properties of two-dimensional (2-D) shapes, including their angles.

Students will continue to build on their knowledge and experiences with the *LogoPaths* Software in Grades 4 and 5.

Introducing the *LogoPaths* Activities

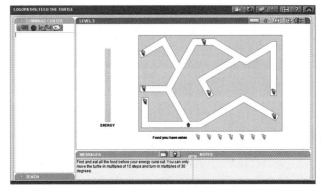

▲ In *Feed the Turtle,* students determine the forward and back steps and turning angles needed to move a turtle through a maze.

In your first introduction of the *Get the Toys* game, show students the following:

- How to open *LogoPaths* by double-clicking on the icon

- How to open *Get the Toys* by clicking on it once

- How to select the level they wish to play

- How to enter forward and back commands in multiples of 10 (e.g., **fd 50** or **bk 100**)

- How to enter command to turn right or left 90° (**rt 90** or **lt 90**)

- How to use the *Label Lengths* and *Label Turns* tools

In your first introduction of the *Missing Measures* and the *200 (400, 500) Steps* activities, show students the following:

- How to open *Free Explore* by clicking on it once

- How to enter forward and back commands of any amount (e.g., **fd 82** or **bk 125**) (Note that move and turn inputs must be between −999 and 999.)

- How to use the **ht** (hide turtle) and **st** (show turtle) commands

- How to use the *Teach Tool* to make a procedure from a set of commands in the Command Center. You will be asked to give it a name, and the commands will be moved to the Teach Window in the proper format for a procedure.

In your first introduction of the *Feed the Turtle* game, show students the following:

- How to open *Feed the Turtle* by clicking on it once

- How to select the level they wish to play

- How to enter forward and back commands of any amount (e.g., **fd 82** or **bk 125**)

- How to enter commands to turn right or left in multiples of 30° (e.g., **rt 30**, **rt 120**, **lt 60**, **lt 180**)

- How to use the *Turtle Turner* and the *Ruler* tool

You can introduce more of the tools available in *LogoPaths* as students indicate interest and the need to use them.

- Students can use the penup (**pu**) and pendown (**pd**) commands to tell the turtle to draw as it moves. Type **pu** in the Command Center to move without drawing. Type **pd** for the turtle to draw as it moves.

- The repeat command tells the turtle to repeat a set of commands a specified number of times. The first input is the number of times to repeat, and the second is a list of commands enclosed in square brackets. For example, to repeat a forward move and a right turn three times, students might type **repeat 3 [fd 100 rt 90]**.

- Students can change the color, shape, and size of the turtle and the line it draws using the turtle features panel . Other features of how the turtle works (e.g., its speed) can be changed in the preferences panel .

- Further information about commands, tools, and buttons can be found in the online help .

It is likely that many students will discover other tools and their uses on their own as they spend more time working with the software. Encourage them to share their discoveries with one another.

Saving Student Work

If you want to discuss students' work later, they should either print it (if your computers are connected to a printer) or save their work on a disk. For information about printing or saving to a disk, see the *Software Support Reference Guide* contained in your curriculum guide package.

Professional Development

Teacher Notes in *Investigations*

Teacher Notes are one of the most important professional development tools in *Investigations*. Each curriculum unit contains a collection of Teacher Notes that offer information about the mathematical content of that unit and how students learn it.

In this section of *Implementing Investigations in Grade 3,* you will find a set of Teacher Notes that addresses topics and issues applicable to the curriculum as a whole rather than to specific curriculum units. These Teacher Notes include the following:

These Teacher Notes provide important background about approaches to mathematics teaching and learning, about critical features of the mathematics classroom, and how to develop an inclusive mathematics community in which all students participate. You can benefit from reading these notes, either individually or as the basis for discussion in teacher study groups, before starting to use the curriculum. Alternatively, you can read these notes gradually throughout the year while you are using the curriculum in your classroom. These brief essays take on new resonance and meaning as you have more experience with student learning and the *Investigations* curriculum. Plan to return to this collection periodically to review the ideas and reflect on the implications for classroom practice.

A complete list of the Teacher Note titles from each of the nine curriculum units is included on pages 74–75.

Computational Fluency and Place Value   48
A discussion of the building blocks of computational fluency in addition, subtraction, multiplication, and division, along with the central role of the base-ten number system in developing fluency

Computation Algorithms and Methods   52
A look at the important characteristics of algorithms students use in the elementary grades, useful nonalgorithmic methods, and the role of the U.S. standard algorithms in the classroom

Representations and Contexts for Mathematical Work   55
A review of the important role of representations and contexts in supporting students' visualization of mathematical relationships and examples of how students use these representations

Foundations of Algebra in the Elementary Grades   60
A discussion of how the *Investigations* units support students' early algebraic thinking

Discussing Mathematical Ideas   65
A look at the importance of discussion as a regular part of your mathematics work

Racial and Linguistic Diversity in the Classroom: What Does Equity Mean in Today's Math Classroom?   68
A reflection on questions and issues of importance in considering the racial, ethnic, cultural, and linguistic diversity of today's classroom and a list of resources for further study

Computational Fluency and Place Value

Computational fluency includes accuracy, flexibility, and efficiency. When fluency with a particular operation is achieved, students can look at the problem as a whole, choose a solution strategy that they can carry out easily without becoming bogged down or losing track of their steps, use their strategy to solve the problem accurately, recognize whether the result is reasonable, and double-check their work. Students who are fluent have a repertoire that includes mental strategies, strategies in which only intermediate steps are jotted down while other steps are carried out mentally, and strategies that require a complete written solution. They are flexible in their choice of algorithm or procedure, and they can use one method to check another.

Developing computational fluency with whole numbers is central to the elementary curriculum. This development includes the building blocks of computation:

- Understanding the base-ten number system and its place value notation

- Understanding the meaning of the operations and their relationships

- Knowing the basic addition and multiplication number combinations (the "facts") and their counterparts for subtraction and division

- Estimating reasonable results

- Interpreting problems embedded in contexts and applying the operations correctly to these problems

- Learning, practicing, and consolidating accurate and efficient strategies for computing

- Developing curiosity about numbers and operations, their characteristics, and how they work

- Learning to articulate, represent, and justify generalizations

At each grade level, computational fluency looks different. Students are progressing in learning the meaning of the four arithmetic operations with whole numbers, developing methods grounded in this meaning, and gradually solving problems of greater difficulty through the grades. At each grade level, benchmarks for whole number computation indicate what is expected of all students by the end of each curriculum unit and each grade, although work at each grade level goes beyond these benchmarks. Gradually, approaches to problems become more efficient, flexible, and accurate. For example, in Grade 1, many students begin the year adding by direct modeling of the problem with objects and counting the sum by ones. By the end of the year, students are expected to start with one of the quantities and count on the other, and for some combinations students "just know" the sum or use known combinations to solve others ("I know $4 + 4 = 8$, so $4 + 5 = 9$"). In Grade 4, many students start the year solving some multiplication problems by skip counting, but by the end of the year, they are expected to solve multidigit multiplication problems by breaking problems into subproblems, based on the distributive property.

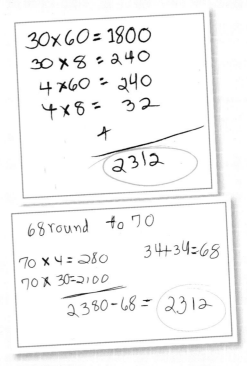

Sample Student Work

Understanding the Base-Ten Number System

Learning about whole number computation is closely connected to learning about the base-ten number system. The base-ten number system is a "place value" system. That is, any numeral, say 2, can represent different values, depending on where it appears in a written number: it can represent 2 ones, 2 tens, 2 hundreds, 2 thousands, as well as 2 tenths, 2 hundredths, and so forth. Understanding this place value system requires coordinating the way we write the numerals that represent a particular number (e.g., 217) and the way we name numbers in words (e.g., two hundred seventeen) with how those symbols represent quantities.

The heart of this work is relating written numerals to the quantity and to how the quantity is composed. It builds from work on tens and ones in Grades 1 and 2 to a focus on numbers in the hundreds and thousands in Grade 3, and work with numbers in the ten thousands, hundred thousands, and beyond in Grades 4 and 5. Knowing place value is not simply a matter of saying that 217 "has 2 hundreds, 1 ten, and 7 ones," which students can easily learn to do by following a pattern without attaching much meaning to what they are saying. Students must learn to visualize how 217 is built up from hundreds, tens, and ones, in a way that helps them relate its value to other quantities. Understanding the place value of a number such as 217 entails knowing, for example, that 217 is closer to 200 than to 300, that it is 100 more than 117, that it is 17 more than 200, that it is 3 less than 220, and that it is composed of 21 tens and 7 ones.

A thorough understanding of the base-ten number system is one of the critical building blocks for developing computational fluency. Understanding place value is at the heart of estimating and computing. For example, consider adding two different quantities to 32:

$32 + 30 = $ _____

$32 + 3 = $ _____

How much will 32 increase in each case? Students think about how the first sum will now have 6 tens, but the ones will not change, whereas in the second sum, the ones will change, but the tens remain the same. Adding three *tens* almost doubles 32, while adding three *ones* increases its value by a small amount. Considering the place value of numbers that are being added, subtracted, multiplied, or divided provides the basis for developing a reasonable estimate of the result.

The composition of numbers from multiples of 1, 10, 100, 1,000, and so forth, is the basis for most of the strategies students adopt for whole number operations. Students' computational algorithms and procedures depend on knowing how to decompose numbers and knowing the effects of operating with multiples of 10. For example, one of the most common algorithms for addition is adding by place. Each number is decomposed into ones, tens, hundreds, and so forth; these parts are then combined. For example,

$326 + 493$

$300 + 400 = 700$

$20 + 90 = 110$

$6 + 3 = 9$

$700 + 110 + 9 = 819$

To carry out this algorithm fluently, students must know a great deal about place value, not just how to decompose numbers. They must also be able to apply their knowledge of single-digit sums such as $3 + 4$ and $2 + 9$ to sums such as $300 + 400$ and $20 + 90$. In other words, they know how to interpret the place value of numbers *as they operate with them*—in this case, that just as 2 ones plus 9 ones equals 11 ones, 2 tens plus 9 tens equals 11 tens, or 110.

As with addition, algorithms for multidigit multiplication also depend on knowing how the place value of numbers is interpreted as numbers are multiplied. Again, students must understand how they can apply knowledge of single-digit combinations such as 3×4 to solve problems such as 36×42.

For example,

36×42

$30 \times 40 = 1,200$

$30 \times 2 = 60$

$6 \times 40 = 240$

$6 \times 2 = 12$

$1,200 + 240 + 60 + 12 = 1,512$

Students gradually learn how a knowledge of 3×4 helps them solve 30×4, 3×40, 30×40, 3×400, and so forth.

Building Computational Fluency Over Time

There is a tremendous amount of work to do in the area of numbers and operations in Grades K–5.

- First graders are still working on coordinating written and spoken numbers with their quantitative meaning.

- Second graders are uncovering the relationship between 10 ones and 1 ten and between 10 tens and 1 hundred.

- Third graders are immersed in how the properties of multiplication differ from the properties of addition.

- Fourth and fifth graders are solving multidigit problems and becoming flexible in their use of a number of algorithms.

This list provides only a brief glimpse of how much work there is to do in these grades.

Students gain computational fluency in each operation through several years of careful development. Extended time across several grades is spent on each operation. Students build computational fluency with small numbers as they learn about the meaning and properties of the operation. Then they gradually expand their work to more difficult problems as they develop, analyze, compare, and practice general methods.

Let's use subtraction as an example of this process:

- In Kindergarten and Grade 1, students solve subtraction problems by modeling the action of subtraction.

- By Grade 2, students are articulating and using the inverse relationship between addition and subtraction to solve problems like the following: "If I have 10 cookies, how many more cookies do I need to bake so I have 24?"

- During Grades 2 and 3, students become fluent with the subtraction "facts" and model and solve a variety of types of subtraction problems, including comparison and missing part problems. By Grade 3, as students' understanding of the base-ten number system grows, they use their understanding of place value to solve problems with larger numbers.

- In Grades 3 and 4, students articulate, represent, and justify important generalizations about subtraction. For example, if you add the same amount to (or subtract it from) each number in a subtraction expression, the difference does not change, as in the equation $483 - 197 = 486 - 200$. In these grades, students also choose one or two procedures, practice them, and expand their command of these procedures with multidigit numbers.

- In Grades 4 and 5, as their fluency with subtraction increases, students analyze and compare strategies for solving subtraction problems. Because they are fluent with more "transparent" algorithms for subtraction in which the place value of the numbers is clear, they are now in a position to appreciate the shortcut notation of the U.S. traditional regrouping algorithm for subtraction, analyze how it works, and compare it to other algorithms. (See the Teacher Note, Computational Algorithms and Procedures.)

[Handwritten note on sticky note: Name Strategies — make a chart]

This account gives only a glimpse of the w[...] understanding subtraction across the grade[...] has a similar complexity. It is critical that t[...] required for the careful development of ideas is devoted to this strand. For this reason, in each of Grades 1–4, there are four units spread throughout the year that focus on whole numbers, operations, and the base-ten number system. In Kindergarten, three units focus on counting, quantity, and modeling addition and subtraction. In Grade 5, because of the increased emphasis on rational numbers, three units focus on whole numbers and two units focus on fractions, decimals, and percents. The whole number units within each grade build on each other in a careful sequence.

As you work with your students on whole number computation, here are some questions to keep in mind as you assess their progress toward computational fluency [adapted from Russell, 2000, p. 158]:

- Do students know and draw on basic facts and other number relationships?

- Do students use and understand the structure of the base-ten number system? For example, do students know the result of adding 100 to 2,340 or multiplying 40×500?

- Do students recognize related problems that can help with the problem?

- Do students use relationships among operations?

- Do students know what each number and numeral in the problem means (including subproblems)?

- Can students explain why the steps being used actually work?

- Do students have a clear way to record and keep track of their procedures?

- Do students have more than one approach for solving problems in each operation? Can they determine which problems lend themselves to different methods?

Supporting Computational Fluency Across the Curriculum

Work in the other content areas also connects to and supports the work on computational fluency in the number and operations units. For example, an emphasis on the foundations of algebra across the grades opens up important opportunities to strengthen work with numbers and operations. Within the number and operations units themselves, articulation, representation, and justification of general claims about the operations (an aspect of early algebraic thinking) strengthen students' understanding of the operations (see the Teacher Note, Foundations of Algebra in the Elementary Grades, and the Algebra Connections essay in each of the number and operations units). The work with functions provides interesting problem contexts in which students' work on ratio and on constant rates of change connect to and support their work on multiplication (see the Teacher Note, Foundations of Algebra in the Elementary Grades, and the Algebra Connections essay in each of the patterns, functions, and change units). Geometry and measurement units also provide contexts in which students revisit multiplication. Finally, the Classroom Routines (in Grades K–3) and Ten-Minute Math (in Grades 3–5) provide ongoing, regular practice of estimation and computation.

Reference

Russell, S. J. (2000). Developing computational fluency with whole numbers. *Teaching Children Mathematics 7*, 154–158.

Computational Algorithms and Methods

In the elementary grades, a central part of students' work is learning about addition, subtraction, multiplication, and division and becoming fluent and flexible in solving whole number computation problems. In the *Investigations* curriculum, students use methods and algorithms in which they can see clearly the steps of their solution and focus on the mathematical sense of what they are doing. They use and compare several different methods to deepen their understanding of the properties of the operations and to develop flexibility in solving problems. They practice methods for each operation so that they can use them efficiently to solve problems.

What Is an Algorithm?

An algorithm is a series of well-defined steps used to solve a certain class of problem (for example, all addition problems). Often, the sequence of steps is repeated with successive parts of the problem. For example, here is an example of an addition algorithm:

$$249 + 674$$

$$200 + 600 = 800$$

$$40 + 70 = 110$$

$$9 + 4 = 13$$

$$800 + 110 + 13 = 923$$

Written instructions for this algorithm might begin as follows:

1. Find the left-most place represented in the addends and add all the amounts in that place.

2. Move one place to the right and add all the amounts in that place in all the addends.

3. Repeat step 2 until all parts of all addends have been added.

4. Add the sums of each place.

To specify these instructions, as if we were going to teach them to a computer, we would have more work to do to make them even more specific and precise. For example, how is step 4 carried out? Should each place be added separately again and then combined? In practice, when students and adults use this algorithm, the partial sums that must be added in step 4 are generally easy enough to add mentally, as they are in this problem, although occasionally one might again break up some of the numbers.

Algorithms like this one, once understood and practiced, are general methods that can be used for a whole class of problems. The adding by place algorithm, for example, can be generalized for use with any addition problem. As students' knowledge of the number system expands, they learn to apply this algorithm to, for example, larger numbers or to decimals. Students also learn how to use clear and concise notation, to carry out some steps mentally, and to record those intermediate steps needed so that they can keep track of the solution process.

Nonalgorithmic Methods for Computing with Whole Numbers

Students also learn methods for computing with whole numbers that are not algorithmic—that is, one cannot completely specify the steps for carrying them out, and they do not generally involve a repetition of steps. However, these methods are studied because they are useful for solving certain problems. In thinking through why and how they work, students also deepen their understanding of the properties of the various operations. This work provides opportunities for students to articulate generalizations about the operations and to represent and justify them.

For example, here is one method a third grader might use to solve this problem:

$$\$7.46 + \$3.28 = \$7.50 + \$3.24 = \$10.74$$

The student changed the addition expression to an equivalent expression with numbers that made it easier to find the sum mentally. First graders often use this idea as they learn some of their addition combinations, transforming a combination they are learning into an equivalent combination they already know: $7 + 5 = 6 + 6 = 12$.

When students try to use the same method to make a subtraction problem easier to solve, they find that they must modify their method to create an equivalent problem. Instead of adding an amount to one number and subtracting it from the other, as in addition, they must add the same amount to (or subtract it from) each number:

$$182 - 69 = 183 - 70 = 113$$

Throughout the *Investigations* curriculum, methods like these are introduced and studied to deepen students' understanding of how these operations work and to engage them in proving their ideas using representations of the operations.

Because the ways in which a problem might be changed to make an equivalent problem that is easier to solve can vary (although it might be possible to precisely specify a particular variant of one of these methods), these methods are not algorithms. Students do not generally use such methods to solve a whole class of problems (e.g., any addition problem); rather, students who are flexible in their understanding of numbers and operations use finding equivalent expressions as one possible method and notice when a problem lends itself to solving in this way.

Learning Algorithms Across the Grades

In *Investigations,* students develop, use, and compare algorithms and other methods. These are not "invented" but are constructed with teacher support, as students' understanding of the operations and the base-ten number system grow (see the Teacher Note, Computational Fluency and Place Value). Because the algorithms that students learn are so grounded in knowledge of the operation and the number system, most of them arise naturally as students progress from single-digit to multidigit problems. For example, the adding by place addition algorithm shown earlier naturally grows out of what students are learning about how a number such as 24 is composed of 2 tens and 4 ones. It is part of the teacher's role to make these methods explicit, help students understand and practice them, and support students to gradually use more efficient methods. For example, a second grader who is adding on one number in parts might solve $49 + 34$ by adding on 10, then another 10, then another 10, then 4 to 49 $(49 + 10 + 10 + 10 + 4)$. By having this student compare solutions with another student's whose first step is $49 + 30$, the teacher helps the first student analyze what is the same and different about their solutions and opens up the possibility for the first student of a more efficient method—adding on a multiple of 10 all at once rather than breaking it into 10s.

The algorithms and other methods that students learn about and use in *Investigations* for multidigit problems are characterized by their *transparency*. Transparent algorithms

• make the properties of the operations visible.

• show the place value of the numbers in the problem.

• make clear how a problem is broken into subproblems and how the results of these subproblems are recombined.

These characteristics are critical for students while they are learning the meaning of the operations and are building their understanding of the base-ten system. Here is an example of a transparent multiplication algorithm that might be used by a fourth grader:

$$
\begin{array}{r}
34 \\
\times\ 78 \\
\hline
2100 \\
280 \\
240 \\
32 \\
\hline
\end{array}
$$

$$2{,}000 + 500 + 150 + 2 = 2{,}652$$

In this algorithm, students record all numbers fully, showing the place value of all the digits. Because the result of each multiplication is shown, the application of the distributive property is kept track of clearly.

There is a misperception that many different algorithms might arise in a single classroom and that this multitude of algorithms will be confusing. In fact, there are only a few basic algorithms and methods for each operation that arise from students' work and that are emphasized in the curriculum. Each is tied closely to how students solve problems and to the basic characteristics and properties of the operation. Teacher Notes throughout the curriculum provide more detail about these methods.

Students can and do develop efficiency and fluency with these more transparent algorithms. As they do, they do some steps mentally and may no longer need to write out every step to keep track of their work. For example, in using the adding by place algorithm to add $249 + 674$, a competent user might simply jot down 800, 110, 13, and then add those partial sums mentally and record the answer. There may be times when you require students to write out their complete solution method so that you can see how they are solving problems, but for everyday use, efficient users of such algorithms will record only the steps they need.

These algorithms and methods are studied, compared, and analyzed for different reasons. All of them are transparent, preserve place value, and make visible important properties such as distributivity. Some can be practiced and provide general, efficient methods. Others are useful only for particular problems but are studied because of what they illuminate about the operations.

Studying the U.S. Standard Algorithms

The U.S. standard algorithms for addition, subtraction, and multiplication are also explicitly studied in *Investigations* but only after students are fully grounded in understanding the operation and using transparent algorithms for multidigit computation. These algorithms were developed for efficiency and compactness for handwritten computation. When these algorithms are used as a primary teaching tool, their very compactness, which can be an advantage for experienced users, becomes a disadvantage for young learners because they obscure the place value of the numbers and the properties of the operation.

Some students do use the standard algorithms with understanding. As these algorithms come up in class, they should be incorporated into the list of class strategies. Teachers should make sure that students who use them understand what the shortcut notation represents and that they can explain why these algorithms make sense. They should also know and understand other methods. In Grade 4, students revisit the U.S. standard addition algorithm formally, analyze how and why it works, and compare it to other algorithms they are using. In Grade 5, students revisit the U.S. standard subtraction and multiplication algorithms in the same way. Division methods studied in this curriculum focus on the inverse relationship between multiplication and division.

Representations and Contexts for Mathematical Work

Mathematics involves describing and analyzing all kinds of mathematical relationships. Throughout the *Investigations* curriculum, students use representations and contexts to help them visualize these mathematical relationships. Thinking with representations and contexts allows students to express and further develop their ideas and enables students to engage with each other's ideas. Whether solving a multiplication problem, finding the area of a rectangle, describing the relationship between two variables, or ordering fractions, students use representations and contexts to investigate and explain.

The *Investigations* curriculum introduces a limited number of carefully chosen representations and contexts because they provide representations of mathematical relationships that students can use to solve problems and/or to show their ideas and solutions to others. Students may first use representations or contexts concretely, drawing or modeling with materials. Later, they incorporate these representations and contexts into mental models that they can call on to visualize the structure of problems and their solutions. Students develop the habit of making drawings, building models, and using representations to think with and to explain their thinking to others. They develop a repertoire of representations that they know well and can apply when faced with unfamiliar problem situations.

Good contexts and representations have the following characteristics:

- They are useful for a whole class of problems (e.g., addition problems).

- They can be extended to accommodate more complex problems and/or students' expanding repertoire of numbers.

- They do not overwhelm or interfere with the focus on mathematical content.

- Their structure embodies important characteristics of the mathematical relationships.

This Teacher Note provides some examples of how models, materials, and contexts are used by students across the grades.

Representations

Basic representations in the *Investigations* curriculum include connecting cubes, the 100 chart (and its variants, the 300, 1,000, and 10,000 charts), number lines, arrays, and sets of two-dimensional (2-D) and three-dimensional (3-D) shapes. Each representation provides access to certain characteristics, actions, and properties of numbers and operations or of geometric properties and relationships. Here are two examples.

Connecting Cubes

Connecting cubes are a basic material for counting and for modeling addition and subtraction in Grades K–2. The cubes are a discrete model of whole numbers and provide a uniform counting material for representing ones. Because they connect, they can be organized into sticks of ten cubes so that students can use them to represent tens and ones.

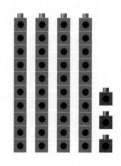

The individual cubes are visible in the connected stick of ten, so students can visualize how this stick represents the equivalence of 1 ten and 10 ones and then how 10 ten-sticks is equivalent to 1 hundred and 100 ones. Connecting cubes are a flexible material. They are well suited for modeling the basic actions of joining and separating. They can also be used to construct rectangular arrays for studying multiplication and area. Students also use the cubes to construct rectangular prisms and to analyze and visualize how the volume of the shape consists of a certain number of layers, each of which has the same dimensions.

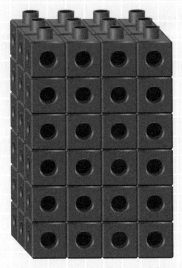

Each layer is 3 × 4. There are six layers.

The Number Line

The number line is another key representation of numbers. This continuous representation offers students another view of the number sequence and number relationships. Students' beginning work with number lines involves number lines that are already marked with the counting numbers.

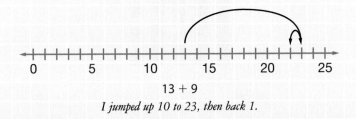

13 + 9

I jumped up 10 to 23, then back 1.

Later, students choose the part of the number line they need and which points on it should be marked as they use it to solve problems.

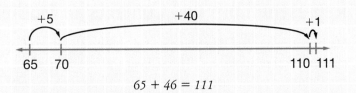

65 + 46 = 111

The number line provides access to the idea that numbers are infinite. At first, students come to this idea in relation to the counting sequence of whole numbers. Later, as they encounter negative numbers, they consider how the number line extends in both directions, that both positive and negative numbers "go on forever." In their study of rational numbers, they use the number line to model fractions and decimal fractions and consider how the segments of the number line between two successive whole numbers can be divided into smaller and smaller pieces. In later years, they will come to understand that there are an infinite number of numbers between any two successive integers.

For students to use a representation well, they need enough experience with it so that they understand its basic characteristics and can then use it themselves to model and solve problems. For example, using an unmarked number line flexibly requires that students have enough prior experience using the marked number line to count and add.

Using Different Representations

Different representations offer different models of the mathematics and access to different mathematical ideas. For example, both place value models and number lines are useful in students' study of subtraction, but they each allow students to see different aspects of subtraction. A student solving the problem 103 − 37 might think about subtracting 37 in parts by visualizing a place value model of the numbers, subtracting 3 tens and then 7 ones (which, for ease of subtraction from 103, the student might split into 3 + 4).

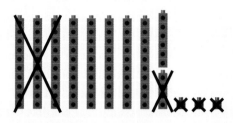

Another student might think about creating an easier, equivalent problem: $103 - 37 = 106 - 40$. This student might visualize "sliding" the interval from 37 to 103 along a number line to determine how to change the numbers, while preserving the difference between them.

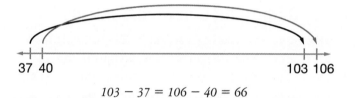

$$103 - 37 = 106 - 40 = 66$$

More details about these and other representations are provided throughout the curriculum units.

Contexts

Contexts and stories are also used to represent mathematical relationships. A good context can be created from familiar events or fantasy. Contexts that students can imagine and visualize give them access to ways of thinking about the mathematical ideas and relationships they are studying. For a context to be useful, it must be connected enough to students' experience that students can imagine and represent the actions and relationships. At the same time, the details of the context need not be elaborate, so that the nonmathematical aspects of the context stay in the background. Here are two examples.

The Penny Jar

One of the contexts in the patterns and functions units in Grades 1 and 4 is the Penny Jar. The Penny Jar contains some number of pennies (the starting amount) and then has a certain number of pennies added to it each day or with each round (the constant rate of change). This is one of the contexts used to engage students in exploring a function—the relationship of the number of days to the total number of pennies—that involves a constant rate of change. Students' knowledge of similar real-world contexts engages students quickly in the mathematics and helps them visualize the mathematical relationships, but it is not so elaborate that it obscures or distracts from the mathematics.

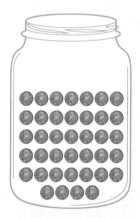

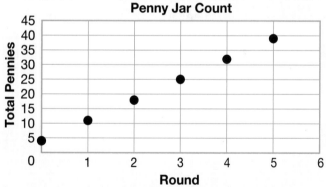

Number of Rounds	Total Number of Pennies
Start	4
1	11
2	18
3	25
4	32
5	39

Once students are familiar with the Penny Jar context, they can represent it in multiple ways, using pictures, tables, and graphs, to describe and analyze the relationship between the two variables.

Travel Stories

In Grade 3, travel stories are used as a context for subtraction. Students are familiar with taking trips by car or bus or have encountered such trips in stories or movies. They know abouta trip having a starting point, an ending point, and a certain distance traveled. They are also familiar with stopping along the way for a meal or to take a break and with discussing how much of the distance has been covered and how much is still ahead of them.

Name _____ Date _____

Collections and Travel Stories

More Travel Problems

Write an equation to represent each problem.
Then solve each one and show your solutions.

1. Last weekend, the McDonald family took the train to Center City. The train traveled 16 miles before stopping at the White Pines station to pick up more passengers. When the train pulled into the Center City station, it had traveled 93 miles in all. How far did the train travel from the White Pines station to Center City?

2. The Chan family visited their cousins last summer. They set the trip meter on their car at 0 before they left home. They stopped at a rest area 42 miles from their home. Later, they stopped to get lunch at a restaurant 100 miles from their home. How far did they travel from the rest area to the restaurant?

3. When the Chan family arrived at their cousins' house, the trip meter read 138 miles. How far did they travel from the rest area to their cousins' house?

58   Unit 3   Session 3.5

© Pearson Education 3

▲ **Grade 3 Unit 3** *Student Activity Book,* **page 58**

Helping Students Connect to Contexts

Teachers often personalize these contexts for students to help them visualize and use it. For example, when using the Penny Jar context, one second-grade teacher had a brief discussion about places they or someone else they know used to hold money and some reasons that money might get added to any of these. The teacher then referred to some of these situations as they discussed problems, "Let's say we're talking about Andre's situation when he is doing his chores. He has 3 pennies in the jar, and he is going to put in 2 pennies for each chore he completes." In using the travel story context, teachers also refer to situations that are familiar to students: "So let's say Janelle and her family are setting off to visit her grandma, like they did last summer, and the whole trip is 274 miles. …"

More details about these and other contexts are provided throughout the curriculum units.

Using Representations and Contexts

Representations and contexts are central in mathematics at all levels for investigating, explaining, and justifying mathematical ideas. Students should move toward developing mental models of mathematical relationships that they call on routinely and will often use pictures, diagrams, and objects when they encounter new kinds of problems.

Students should use representations and contexts judiciously and with purpose. A first grader who is solving word problems that involve addition and subtraction might model every problem with cubes. Another student in the same class might model one or two problems; then, having visually confirmed the action of the operation, the student might solve the rest by imagining one quantity and counting on. A third student—or the same student later in the year—might reason about the numbers without using an image or model. In class discussions, both the teacher and students use representations to clarify and investigate mathematical ideas and to help all students focus on what is being discussed.

As a teacher, one of your roles is to support students in using representations and contexts and to help them develop mental images that they can call on. On the one hand, students need not show a picture for a problem when they have developed more efficient numerical tools and methods. For example, when one fourth grader was asked to solve a multiplication problem in two ways, he solved the problem by breaking it up efficiently, using the distributive property, and then showed a solution using groups of tally marks. His teacher let him know that using tally marks was not what she was looking for from him and reminded him of the work the class had been doing on changing one of the numbers in the problem and then adjusting the product.

On the other hand, students should understand that the use of representations and models is not a "crutch" in mathematics but are a powerful set of tools for investigating problem situations. In the classroom, encourage representation as a central part of mathematics activity. Make a habit of asking questions such as these:

- Is there a way you can show us your thinking using the number line or the 100 chart?

- Can you explain how your strategy makes sense using the travel context we have been using for some of the problems?

- You used a number line and Chris used a place-value sketch showing tens and ones. What is similar or different about these two approaches? Where can you see the four tens in Chris's place value sketch on Luc's number line solution?

- Karen, you are thinking of the multiplication problem as representing 47 classrooms with 23 students in each class. How did this context help you keep track of the parts of the problem?

- Can you show us with a picture or on the Geoboard what you mean when you say "a triangle is half of a rectangle"?

- What if you needed to explain or prove what you are saying to someone who came to visit our classroom? Is there a way you can show me why what you are saying is true with a picture or diagram?

When students are accustomed to incorporating representations in their daily mathematics work and considering what representations can be helpful for explaining mathematical ideas, they can also create their own images appropriate to a particular problem situation. Help students make these images simple enough so that they serve the mathematics rather than obscure it. The use of representations in class discussions helps illuminate students' ideas for each other and, by putting out an image that is available to all students, clarifies what mathematical relationships are being considered and invites more students into the conversation.

For further examples of students' use of representations, see the classroom stories in the section "Language and Representation" in Part 7, Working with the Range of Learners: Classroom Cases.

Foundations of Algebra in the Elementary Grades

Algebra is a multifaceted area of mathematics content that has been described and classified in different ways. Across many of the classification schemes, four areas foundational to the study of algebra stand out: (1) generalizing and formalizing patterns; (2) representing and analyzing the structure of numbers and operations; (3) using symbolic notation to express functions and relations; and (4) representing and analyzing change.

In the *Investigations* curriculum, these areas of early algebra are addressed in two major ways: (1) work within the counting, number, and operations units focusing on generalizations that arise in the course of students' study of numbers and operations and (2) a coherent strand, consisting of one unit in each grade, K–5, that focuses on patterns, functions, and change. These two areas of emphasis are described here, followed by some additional information about the goals of work on early algebra in the curriculum.

Early Algebra: Making General Claims About Numbers and Operations

Each *Investigations* unit on counting, numbers, and operations includes a focus on reasoning and generalizing about numbers and operations. Even in beginning work with numbers and operations in Kindergarten and Grade 1, students are already noticing regularities about numbers and operations. For example, in the K–1 game *Double Compare*, each student in the pair selects two number cards. The student with the greater sum says "me." In this early work, before students know their single-digit addition combinations, most students are counting all or counting on to determine the sum. But consider how students are reasoning in the following brief episode:

> Bridget and Siva are playing *Double Compare*. Bridget draws a 5 and a 2; Siva draws a 5 and a 3 and immediately says "me," indicating that he has the greater sum. Siva usually counts both amounts by ones to get the sum, so the teacher asks him, "How did you know you have more?" Siva responds, "Because I have a 3 and she has a 2, and 3 is bigger." Bridget is nodding vigorously and adds, "The 5s don't count."

How are the students in this episode figuring out who has the greater sum? Why does Siva only compare 3 with 2, and what does Bridget mean when she says the "5s don't count"? Implicit in these students' work is a general claim about adding numbers that many young students use: If you are comparing two addition expressions, and one of the addends in the first expression is the same as one of the addends in the second, then you need only compare the other two addends to determine which expression has the greater sum. This is a mouthful to put into words, and students might not be able to articulate this idea completely; nevertheless, they are reasoning based on this idea. In later years, this idea can be represented with symbolic notation:

For any numbers a, b, c, and d when $a = c$ and $b < d$, then $a + b < c + d$.

$a = c$	$b <$	$a + b < c + d$
$5 = 5$	$2 < 3$	$5 + 2 < 5 + 3$

Part of the teaching work in the elementary grades is to help students articulate, represent, investigate, and justify such general claims that arise naturally in the course of their work with numbers and operations. In each of the number and operations units in Grades K–5, the Algebra Connections essay highlights several of these general ideas about properties and relationships relevant to the work in that curriculum unit, with examples of how students think about and represent them. Investigation and discussion of some of these generalizations are built into unit sessions; for others, Algebra Notes alert the teacher to activities or discussions in which these ideas are likely to arise and could be pursued.

In the course of articulating, representing, and justifying their ideas about such general claims, students in the elementary grades are beginning to engage in proving—a central part of mathematics. They consider the questions: Does this generalization apply to *all* numbers (in the domain under consideration, usually whole numbers)? Why does it work? How do you know? In two of the number and operations units in each grade, 2–5, you will find a Teacher Note that focuses on proof and justification. These Teacher Notes provide examples of the ways that students at that grade level engage in proving and how their proofs, based on representations, are related to the proofs a mathematician might carry out.

Examples of the general claims highlighted in the curriculum in Grades K–2 are as follows:

- Counting the same set of objects in different orders results in the same count.

- If one number is larger than another, and the same number is added to each, the first total will be larger than the second: $3 + 5 > 2 + 5$.

- You can add two numbers in either order: $6 + 3 = 3 + 6$.

- If you add an amount to one addend and subtract it from another addend, the sum remains the same: $6 + 6 = 12$; $7 + 5 = 12$.

- Addition and subtraction are related. If adding two numbers gives a certain sum, then subtracting one of the addends from the sum results in the other addend: $6 + 7 = 13$; $13 - 7 = 6$; $13 - 6 = 7$.

- You can break numbers into parts to add them: $6 + 8 = 6 + (4 + 4) = (6 + 4) + 4$.

- If you add two even numbers, the sum is even. If you add two odd numbers, the sum is even. If you add an even number and an odd number, the sum is odd.

Some of the generalizations investigated in Grades K–2 are revisited in Grades 3–5 with higher numbers and more complex problems. In addition, new general claims are investigated. Examples of general claims highlighted in Grades 3–5 are as follows:

- If you add the same amount to both numbers in a subtraction problem, the difference does not change: $145 - 97 = 148 - 100$.

- You can multiply two numbers in either order: $32 \times 20 = 20 \times 32$.

- You can break numbers into parts to multiply them, but each part of each number must be multiplied by each part of the other number: $7 \times 24 = 7 \times (20 + 4) = (7 \times 20) + (7 \times 4)$.

- Multiplication and division are related. If multiplying two numbers gives a certain product, then dividing that product by one of the original factors results in the other factor: $9 \times 8 = 72$; $72 \div 8 = 9$; $72 \div 9 = 8$.

- A factor of a number is a factor of multiples of that number: 3 is a factor of 15; 15 is a factor of 30, so 3 is a factor of 30.

- If you double (or triple) one of the factors in a multiplication problem and halve (or third) the other, the product remains the same: $164 \times 4 = 328 \times 2$.

Early Algebra: Patterns, Functions, and Change

Investigations includes a coherent K–5 strand on patterns, functions, and change, with one unit in each grade. The content of these units starts with repeating patterns and number sequences in Grades K and 1, connects these patterns and sequences to functional relationships beginning in Grade 2, and then develops ideas about linear and nonlinear contexts that involve relationships between two variables in Grades 3–5. In each of these units in K–5, the Algebra Connections essay highlights some of the ideas students work on in that unit, and how they connect to later work in algebra.

Patterns and Functions in Grades K–2

Work with repeating patterns has long been a staple of mathematics work in the primary grades, but it often seems to have little connection to work in later grades. In the *Investigations* sequence, students' study of the structure of repeating patterns is connected to work with ratios and linear functions by associating the repeating pattern with the counting numbers. Consider this example:

> Students have been building repeating color patterns using connecting cubes. This red-blue-green repeating pattern has been numbered with the counting numbers, starting with 1. Students are considering which numbers are associated with the green cubes:

> 1 2 3 4 5 6 7 8 9 10 11 12

> Kamala says that the greens have a "counting by 3s" pattern: 3, 6, 9, 12. Esperanza says, "it will always be on the threes because every time you skip two, then it's green." Theo adds, remembering a previous Investigation in which they built buildings from connecting cubes with the same number of cubes in each layer: "It's like the same pattern we made when we made the building. It's always adding threes. One floor is three, two floors is six, and you keep adding three— 3, 6, 9, um, 12, and you keep going by 3s."

Students are recognizing the underlying 1:3 ratio in both situations. In the repeating pattern, there is a relationship between the position of each green cube among all green cubes and its position among all the cubes: the *first* green is in position 3 in the sequence, the *second* green in position 6, the *third* green in position 9, and so forth. In the cube building, there are 3 cubes for each floor: one floor has

3 cubes, 2 floors have 6 cubes, 3 floors have 9 cubes, and so forth. These constant ratio situations are students' first examples of linear change—change at a constant rate.

Examples of ideas investigated in Grades K–2 in these units are as follows:

- Repeating patterns can be described as iterations of a unit. This repeating color pattern can be divided into its units, the part that repeats:

- When the elements of a repeating pattern are numbered with the counting numbers, elements in the pattern can be characterized by a particular number sequence. In a red-blue-red-blue connecting cube train, the blue cubes are numbered 2, 4, 6, 8, . . . , and the red cubes are numbered 1, 3, 5, 7, ...

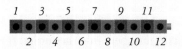

- The same number sequence can represent different situations. The blue cubes in a red-blue repeating pattern and the claps in a tap-clap repeating pattern fall in the same numbered positions.

- In a ratio situation, as one quantity changes by a certain amount, the other quantity always changes by a certain amount (for each day, there are 3 pennies added to the jar).

- Tables are a representation that can be used to show how one variable changes in relation to another.

- The same ratio relationship can occur in different contexts (e.g., 3 pennies per day, 3 cubes per "floor").

Patterns, Functions, and Change in Grades 3–5

In Grades 3–5, students focus on both linear and nonlinear change. Students study situations with a constant rate of change, in which two variables are related in ways that can be expressed in a verbal rule or an equation (such as the relationship between the total number of pennies in a jar and the number of days pennies have been collected, when a fixed number of pennies is added to the jar each day). They learn to take into account any starting amount (i.e., the number of pennies in the jar at the beginning) and the rate of change (i.e., the number of pennies added to the jar each day). They also study relationships in which the value of one variable cannot be determined based on the value of the other (such as the relationship between temperature and time in Grade 3 and between plant growth and time in Grade 4). In Grades 4 and 5, they also encounter situations in which the relationship between the two variables can be determined, but the change is not occurring at a constant rate, for example, a Penny Jar in which the number of pennies doubles each day.

Students work extensively with ways of representing relationships between two variables: with words, with tables and graphs, with numbers, and (starting in Grade 4) with symbolic notation. These units reinforce and connect with work in other units on multiplication, ratio, area, volume, and graphing. The Algebra Connections essay in each of the patterns, functions, and change units provides more detailed information about this sequence of students' work and how it connects to algebra.

Examples of ideas investigated in these units in Grades 3–5 (in addition to some of those in the K–2 list that continue to be studied in new contexts) are as follows:

- Line graphs are a representation that can show the relationship between two variables. A line graph represents both individual values of the variable and the rate of change of one variable in relation to another.

- In a situation with a constant rate of change, the value of one variable can be determined, given the value of the other.

- The relationship between two variables in a situation with a constant rate of change can be described in words and with symbolic notation.

- In some situations, the rate of change is determined but not constant. In these situations, the rate of change may be, for example, increasing by a constant amount.

Early Algebra Is Fundamental

Underlying the work in early algebra are, according to one of the *Investigations'* mathematician advisors, "foundational principles"—principles that connect elementary students' work in arithmetic to later work in algebra. For example, when second graders consider how changing the order of numbers in an addition or subtraction problem affects the sum or difference, they can engage in reasoning about foundational ideas, in this case, that addition is commutative, but subtraction is not: $a + b = b + a$, but $c - d \neq d - c$. Even though they may not yet have the experience with negative numbers to allow them to completely make sense of $14 - 26$, they see, through modeling and representing this problem, that it does not have the same difference as $26 - 14$. In later years, they will come to see that there *is* a regularity here, that if $c - d = a$, then $d - c = -a$, or $c - d = -(d - c)$.

Similarly, when fifth graders develop representations to show why halving one factor in a multiplication problem and doubling the other results in the same product, they are applying knowledge of foundational properties of multiplication and division. In later years, they may explain the more general claim that dividing one factor by any number (except 0) and multiplying the other factor by the same number maintains the same product by reference to the associative property of multiplication and to multiplication by 1—the identity element for multiplication. Through a series of steps, based on these properties of multiplication, one can show that, if a, b, and n are numbers $\left(n \neq 0\right)$, then $a \times b = a \times b \times \frac{n}{n} = (a \times n) \times \left(\frac{b}{n}\right)$.

For most adults, notation such as the use of variables, operations, and equal signs is the chief identifying feature of algebra. Although students use symbolic notation in Grades 4 and 5, the notation is not the focus of activity in Grades K–5. Underlying the notation are ways of reasoning about how the operations work. This *reasoning* about how numbers can be put together and taken apart under different operations or about relationships between two changing quantities, *not* the notation, is the central work of elementary students in algebra.

Algebra for All Students

Work in early algebra in the elementary classroom has the potential of enhancing the learning of *all* students. The teachers with whom the *Investigations* team collaborated during the development of the curriculum commented on this potential in their classrooms. Teacher collaborators reported that students who tend to have difficulty in mathematics become stronger mathematical thinkers through this work. As one teacher wrote, "When I began to work on generalizations with my students, I noticed a shift in my less capable learners. Things seemed more accessible to them." When the generalizations are made explicit—through language and representations used to justify them—they become accessible to more students and can become the foundation for greater computational fluency. Furthermore, the disposition to create a representation when a mathematical question arises supports students in reasoning through their confusions.

At the same time, students who generally outperform their peers in mathematics find this content challenging and stimulating. The study of numbers and operations extends beyond efficient computation to the excitement of making and proving conjectures about mathematical relationships that apply to an infinite class of numbers. A teacher explained, "Students develop a habit of mind of looking beyond the activity to search for something more, some broader mathematical context to fit the experience into."

Early algebra is not an add-on. The foundations of algebra arise naturally throughout students' work with numbers, operations, and patterns and by using familiar and accessible contexts to investigate how one set of values changes in relation to another. This work anchors students' concepts of the operations and underlies greater computational flexibility.

Discussing Mathematical Ideas

Throughout the *Investigations* curriculum, whole-class discussion is a key aspect of students' mathematical activity. Class discussion provides a time for students to

- articulate their mathematical ideas.

- share different approaches to solving a problem.

- identify and investigate what they don't understand.

- analyze why a solution works or how it is flawed.

- pose conjectures and identify evidence to support them.

- collaborate to build ideas or solve problems.

- develop mathematical language.

- use representations to describe mathematical relationships.

- compare and connect students' various ideas, representations, and solutions.

- learn to consider and question each other's ideas.

By carefully selecting problems, representations, and solutions for the whole class to consider, the teacher focuses discussion on key mathematical ideas and works with the class as a whole to move students' thinking forward.

Building Mathematical Community

In the first weeks of school, teachers help the class develop norms for classroom discussion and work with students on attitudes and behavior that will support productive math discussions. Most teachers find that they need to work quite explicitly with students throughout the school year to first establish and then maintain expectations for class discussion. During discussions, teachers keep the flow of ideas organized and remind students about the appropriate focus. For example, "Right now I want comments that are either agreeing with, disagreeing with, or commenting on Yolanda's idea," or "So we now have three different approaches to this problem on the board. Is there a way in which Jill's is similar to Corey's?" Teachers also find opportunities to comment directly on student actions, behavior, and contributions that support productive discourse:

> Because Stephen was willing to talk through what was confusing him when he got an answer that he knew wasn't right, it seemed to really help all of us understand this kind of problem better.

> When Kamala put up her picture of the problem, I heard some of you say, "Ooh!" What was it you understood when you saw that picture? Did anyone else have a picture or a diagram that helped you understand how to solve this problem?

And from time to time teachers discuss directly with the class what aspects of class discussions have been helping or hindering students' participation:

> What helps you be willing to share your work or make an observation during class discussion? Are there times you don't feel comfortable speaking? Why is that?

Building an inclusive mathematics classroom involves a focus on respect for student ideas and acceptance of differences. Working on establishing this community with students will vary across grades and even from one year to another, depending on the needs and experiences of your students. (See the section "Setting Up the Mathematical Community" in Part 7, Working with the Range of Learners: Classroom Cases for some teachers' thoughts on building the classroom mathematics community.)

Focusing Class Discussions

Students' ideas are important and are, in fact, central to discussion. But if a discussion bounces among too many different ideas or tries to include too many different approaches, the discussion becomes ungrounded and hard for students to follow. Simply listing one problem-solving approach after another doesn't engage students beyond the few moments when they are contributing their own idea.

The Math Focus Points for Discussion and sample teacher dialogue found in the text for every discussion will help you guide the discussion. In preparing for class, ask yourself:

- What do I want this discussion to accomplish?

- What do I want all students to take away from this discussion?

- How will the time spent as a whole class enhance the work students have done individually or in pairs or groups?

During work that precedes the discussion, observe students' work with the upcoming discussion in mind. Ask yourself:

- What is a difficulty that many students are having?

- What is a problem that many students are struggling with?

- Is there a question that one pair or group came up with that it would be fruitful for the whole class to discuss?

- What are the basic approaches to solving this problem that students are using?

- Which students or groups have ideas or approaches that should be shared?

Student Participation

Whole-class discussion time is precious class time; it should serve to consolidate or move ahead the math thinking of all students. Find ways during discussions to elicit responses from different students. Although all students may not participate in any one discussion, all of your students' voices should be heard over the course of several discussions. There are many ways to work with students to encourage them to participate. For example, listen carefully to students' ideas and look carefully at their work during activities. Help particular students prepare to share one of their ideas. At first, some students might be more comfortable if you put their solution, representation, or idea on the board or a

transparency and present it to the class yourself; alternatively, the student might explain a certain part of the solution, while you add to the student's explanation.

Think of ways to invite all students' participation during each discussion by asking students to raise hands if they used the same approach or if they agree or disagree with a statement you or another student makes. Pose a question and have students discuss it for a few minutes in pairs before having the whole class consider it. Use wait time judiciously and think about ways that students can use quiet signals when they are ready to respond (e.g., thumbs up rather than hands waving); then students who are still thinking are not distracted.

Ideas are bound to come up that you cannot pursue during class discussions. Sometimes you cannot follow or decipher a student's idea at the moment or you are not sure about how it relates to what is being discussed. If you don't understand what a student is saying, you might ask another student to interpret or talk to the student later. Don't be afraid to let students know that you have to think about something and get back to them or follow up with them after the discussion. You can always bring an idea back to the class later if you decide it would be important for the class to think about it.

You can find other ways to follow up a student's idea that is not central or accessible for the whole class: "I was thinking about your idea, and here's a problem I thought you could try it on." Some teachers have a "parking lot" poster for ideas that come up during class but don't have time to pursue. These ideas may come up again later or can be referred to when they become relevant. The better you know the curriculum, the more you will know when they might come up.

Setting Up the Classroom for Discussion

It is critical that students are sitting in such a way that everyone is focused on the discussion and everyone can hear. If there are representations that students need to see during the discussions, they must be large enough and dark enough so that everyone can see them.

A variety of seating arrangements for class discussions can work, as long as there are clear expectations connected to them. In some classrooms, students gather on a rug for the class meeting and then return to their places or choose places for work time. In other classrooms, students often stay at their own desks for meetings. Some teachers vary the setting, with students staying at their desks when the meeting will be short and gathering together when a longer time is needed.

To facilitate a smooth transition to meeting on the rug, some teachers assign students places to sit on the rug, changing them every month or so. Others place circles, mats, or white boards to clearly mark the places available for students to sit. Others allow students to sit wherever they want in a circle as long as they can see the teacher and all of the other students. They might remind students to make a good choice about sitting in a position and next to classmates that enables them to focus on the discussion. While some students can pay attention while sitting on the floor, others do better in a chair.

Guidelines for Whole-Class Discussions

In summary, here are some guidelines to keep in mind for your class's whole-group discussions:

- Set up norms and review them frequently; point out examples in which they are working.

- Plan a clear purpose and focus for each discussion, based on the listed Focus Points.

- Use wait time to give students time to think.

- Ask students to use quiet student signals to indicate they are ready to respond.

- Prepare with some students ahead of time to participate in the discussion.

- Have clear visuals that everyone can see and refer to.

- Establish a routine arrangement that ensures that everyone can hear and see.

- Select only a few students to share solutions.

When all students come to a discussion prepared to listen actively and to contribute ideas, the class discussions provide an important forum in which they can articulate, represent, connect, and consolidate the mathematical ideas they have been working on.

Racial and Linguistic Diversity in the Classroom: What Does Equity Mean in Today's Math Classroom?

… we have no patterns for relating across our human differences as equals. As a result, those differences have been misnamed and misused in the service of separation and confusion.[1]

Audre Lorde

We must not, in trying to think about how we can make a big difference, ignore the small daily differences we can make which, over time, add up to big differences that we often cannot foresee.[2]

Marian Wright Edelman

U.S. public schools are responsible for educating students who are more racially and linguistically diverse than at any other time in our history. The beginning of the 21st century in the United States is marked by an influx of immigrants, and schools and teachers are at the front door meeting these students. Hence, many teachers work in classrooms with increasing numbers of immigrant students, students of color, and linguistically diverse students who often face unique challenges related to language proficiency, cultural and social adaptation, and poverty. What are the issues and challenges for teachers in these diverse classrooms?

While developing this curriculum, the *Investigations* staff and field-test teachers worked together to continue educating ourselves about this question. Many of us have had direct experience teaching in schools where students come from diverse racial, cultural, and linguistic backgrounds. In many cases, the students' culture, race, ethnicity, and first language are different from those of the teacher. This Teacher Note provides a glimpse into the complex issues about racial,

cultural, and linguistic diversity being discussed in the field of education today. It also provides resources for further reading, including those we found helpful in our own professional development.

Equity in the Mathematics Classroom

Equity does not mean that every student should receive identical instruction; instead, it demands that reasonable and appropriate accommodations be made as needed to promote access and attainment for all students. (NCTM, 2000, p. 11)

Investigations was developed with the assumption that all learners can engage in challenging and substantive mathematics. Assumptions about students' capacity and inclination to learn in school can undermine their access to and participation in significant mathematics learning. An extensive body of literature documents the persistence of these assumptions and their effects on students' opportunity to learn. For example, students of color and those whose first language is not English are often seen in terms of what they lack instead of what they bring to the learning environment (termed in the literature a *deficit thinking* model). Student underperformance in school may be explained by student and family shortcomings, behavior that does not match a particular set of norms, immaturity, or lack of intelligence. Students who do not speak fluent English may be judged as having poor or underdeveloped conceptual understanding because they cannot yet express the complexity of their thinking in English. Misunderstanding cultural differences can lead schools to inappropriately place children into special education and low-ability groups and to expect less from them than from other children. For instance, Entwistle and Alexander (1989) report that poor black children are often described as less mature, and, consequently, school personnel may hold lower expectations for them than for children whose socioeconomic status is higher.

---

[1] From a paper delivered at the Copeland Colloquium, Amherst College, in April, 1980. The paper was entitled, "Age, Race, Class, and Sex: Women Redefining Difference."

[2] Marian Wright Edelman, "Families in Peril: An Agenda for Social Change," The W. E. B. Du Bois Lectures (Cambridge, Mass.: Harvard University Press, 1987), p. 107.

Many teachers are working hard to improve learning opportunities for these students, with the goal of enhancing both the learning climate and students' educational performance. In this work, teachers must consider the broader issues as well as practices, procedures, strategies, and other key aspects of schooling. In an educational setting, equity indicates a state in which all children—students of color and white students, males and females, successful students and those who have fallen behind, and students who have been denied access in the past—have equal opportunities to learn, participate in challenging programs, and have equal access to the services they need to benefit from that education. Equity has sometimes been oversimplified to mean that all students should be treated the same—neutrally and without differentiation. Rather, differences matter, and matter in specific ways. Successful learning experiences depend on teachers building on the contributions of all students and recognizing the differences that matter to them.

In the mathematics education literature, researchers from four projects, three in the United States and one in South Africa, looked across their projects to identify features of classrooms "essential for supporting students' understanding" in mathematics (Hiebert et al., 1997). They organize these in five dimensions, one of which is "equity and accessibility." The authors describe this dimension as fundamental:

> [E]quity . . . is not an add-on or an optional dimension. It is an integral part of a system of instruction that sets students' understanding of mathematics as the goal. Without equity, the other dimensions are restricted and the system does not function well. (p. 12)

Race and Linguistic Diversity

While teaching a seminar on race in education several years ago, one of the authors of this essay was met with a remarkable silence and little open discussion of race, racism, and the ways they come up in classroom teaching. Some think that racism is no longer an issue in schools, and that "color blindness" is the way to approach a diverse class of students. However, many in the field believe that explicit classroom attention to race, ethnicity, and home language results in increased communication and learning.

Race (or ethnicity) can have overlapping and coexisting categories of meaning. Sometimes, race signifies being economically, socially, politically, and educationally oppressed. Other times it signifies a sense of community and belonging, involving valuable associations with a particular group, history, cultural codes, and sensibilities. Race conveys multiple meanings, and racism takes on multiple forms, subject to context and situation. Whether expressed subtly or with crude directness, the effects of racism are felt in everyday school experience. Preconceptions about who students are, which are based on surface behaviors, can mask important potential.

For example, in one classroom, a Hmong girl is quiet, well behaved, and does little to demand attention. But although she is well behaved, she is not engaged and does not quite know what's going on in the lesson. In another classroom, a young black boy is distracted and disruptive, eager to contribute, but often "in trouble." The Hmong girl might be seen as a model student—quiet, hard working, high achieving, and nonchallenging of classroom norms. In contrast, the black boy might be seen as loud, threatening, noncompliant, dysfunctional, and low achieving. The characterization of the Hmong girl seems positive, even flattering, in comparison to the characterization of the black boy. However, both views may be silencing the voices, needs, and potential contributions of these children in different ways. For the Hmong girl, a focus on seemingly compliant behavior may lead the teacher to ignore her educational needs. For the black boy, a focus on seemingly bad behavior may distract the teacher from recognizing his educational strengths.

To understand all students' experiences—to support them in rigorous learning and to respect the variety of their language practices, histories, and identities—educators must continue to learn about the issues of race and racism, cultural and linguistic diversity, and teaching practices and strategies that support the learning of all students.

Teaching Practices and Strategies

Many important insights about teaching practices and strategies that support students of color and English language learners can be gleaned from those who have been studying and writing in the field. Some of these educators and researchers focus specifically on the mathematics classroom, but there are also accounts from science and literacy that have a great deal to offer the teaching of mathematics.

Gloria Ladson-Billings studied exemplary teachers of African-American students and has written about an approach of "culturally relevant teaching." Although the teachers she studied differed in the way they structured their classrooms—some appeared more "traditional," while others were more "progressive" in their teaching strategies—their conceptions of and beliefs about teaching and learning had many commonalities. Here is a subset of characteristics of these teachers adapted from Ladson-Billings' list (1995). These teachers

- believed that all students are capable of academic success.

- saw their pedagogy as always in process.

- developed a community of learners.

- encouraged students to learn collaboratively and be responsible for each other.

- believed that knowledge is shared, recycled, and constructed.

- believed they themselves must be passionate about learning.

- believed they must scaffold, or build bridges, to facilitate learning.

- believed assessment must be multifaceted.

Overall, these teachers supported their students and held them to high standards:

> Students were not permitted to choose failure in their classrooms. They cajoled, nagged, pestered, and bribed

the students to work at high intellectual levels. Absent from their discourse was the "language of lacking." . . . Instead, teachers talked about their own shortcomings and limitations and ways they needed to change to ensure student success. (p. 479)

Critical to teaching students who bring a variety of cultural, social, and linguistic experience into the classroom is what Marilyn Cochran-Smith (1995b) calls "understanding children's understanding":

> [C]entral to learning to teach in a culturally and linguistically diverse society is understanding children's understanding or exploring what it means to know a child, to consider his or her background, behaviors, and interactions with others, and to try to do what Duckworth calls "give reason" to the ways the child constructs meanings and interpretations, drawing on experiences and knowledge developed both inside and outside the classroom. (p. 511)

Eleanor Duckworth, whom Cochran-Smith cites above, may have originated the phrase *understanding children's understanding* in her essay of the same name (1996). In that essay, she discusses the idea of "giving children reason" as she describes a group of teachers in a study group who set themselves this challenge: "[E]very time a child did or said something whose meaning was not immediately obvious . . . [they] sought to understand the way in which . . . [it] could be construed to make sense" (pp. 86–87).

This work of hearing and understanding students' ideas, discourse, and representations and involving all of them in significant intellectual work can be especially challenging when students come from backgrounds quite different from the teacher's own. Cindy Ballenger's *Teaching Other People's Children* (1999) and Vivian Paley's *White Teacher* (1989) provide first-person accounts of teachers who are actively examining their own preconceptions about the behavior and discourse of the students they teach. Ballenger expresses how her initial belief that all students' could learn was not enough:

I began with these children expecting deficits, not because I believed they or their background was deficient—I was definitely against such a view—but because I did not know how to see their strengths . . . I came to see . . . strengths . . . that are part of an intellectual tradition, not always a schooled tradition, but an intellectual one nonetheless, and one that, therefore, had a great deal to say to teaching and learning. (p. 3)

Ballenger recounts her journey in learning to listen to the sense of her students, both "honoring the child's home discourse" and engaging the student in "school-based and discipline-based ways of talking, acting, and knowing" (p. 6).

Working in English with students whose first language is not English presents two challenges to teachers who do not share the student's first language: (1) how to learn about, respect, and support the discourse practices that students can contribute from their own knowledge and communities; and (2) how to bring students into the language of the discipline of mathematics in English. Judit Moschkovich (1999) identifies two critical functions of mathematical discussions for English language learners: "uncovering the mathematical content in student contributions and bringing different ways of talking and points of view into contact" (p. 11). She identifies several important instructional strategies that support these students' participation in math discussions (p. 11):

- using several expressions for the same concept

- using gestures and objects to clarify meaning

- accepting and building on student responses

- revoicing student statements with more technical terms

- focusing not only on vocabulary development but also on mathematical content and argumentation practices

Josiane Hudicourt-Barnes (2003) writes about the participation of students whose home language is Haitian Creole. Her research highlights the way that understanding the forms of discourse students contribute from their own culture enables teachers to uncover and appreciate how students are making sense of subject matter. Although she writes about science learning, her observations are applicable to the mathematics classroom: "To be 'responsive to the children and responsible to the subject matter' (Ball, 1997, p. 776), we must be able to hear children's diverse voices and create opportunities for them to pursue their ideas and questions (p. 17)." Further, she argues that classroom discourse that follows a rigid, restrictive format "may mean that children from families of non-Western traditions are shut out of classroom participation and that skills from other traditions are devalued and subtracted from children's cognitive repertoires, and therefore also made unavailable to their fellow students" (p. 17).

Being "responsive to the children and responsive to the subject matter" is highlighted by many of the writers in this field. They emphasize that the teacher's responsibility is *both* to the students' ideas, sense making, and forms of discourse *and* to bringing these students in to the ideas, vocabulary, and ways of working in the discipline of the content area. Gloria Ladson-Billings (2002) sums up her observations of a teacher whose urban, largely African American, students, initially hated writing:

To meet the academic goals he had set, Carter had to rethink his practice in some fundamental ways. . . . He had to keep a sense of uncertainty and a willingness to question in the forefront of his teaching. . . . while Carter empathized with the students' struggle to write he understood that his job was to teach them to do it. He didn't put them down for not enjoying writing or writing well, but he also did not let them off the hook. He had to help them appreciate the power and fulfillment of writing and he had to preserve each student's sense of self. (p. 118)

Continuing to Learn

Continuing to learn is something we all can do. This Teacher Note attempts only to introduce you to some authors and resources who can contribute to that learning. Many of the resources cited here include rich examples from classrooms that can evoke productive interaction when read and discussed with peers. You may have opportunities to take advantage of courses, seminars, or study groups, such as the one that Lawrence and Tatum (1997) describe, or to self-organize peer discussions of articles in the field.

Teachers can also pose their own questions and study their own classrooms. Writing brief case studies in which you raise your own questions about these issues in your teaching and then sharing your writing can be a rich source of learning. You might start by reading what other teachers have written about their own practice as they reflect on their teaching of diverse students. For example, in *What's Happening in Math Class?* (Schifter, 1996), Alissa Sheinbach writes about three students who are struggling in mathematics (vol. 1, pp. 115–129), Allen Gagnon writes about his Spanish-speaking students (vol. 1, pp. 129–136), and Nora Toney recounts her own experiences with racism as a student (when she was bused into a largely white school) and later as a teacher herself (vol. 2, pp. 26–36). After describing some successful experiences in mathematics she had as an adult that contrasted with her experience in the "low group" as a student, Toney concludes by identifying factors that have been important to her own learning:

> I have discovered the ingredients necessary for me to learn and achieve success: high teacher expectation, fairness, inclusiveness, engaging contextual material, constant monitoring and feedback, discussions/debates, and reflective writing. Generally speaking, I need numerous opportunities to connect my thinking and ideas to new concepts and ideas. These factors facilitated my *learning* of mathematics, so now I am trying to incorporate these same factors into *teaching* mathematics. (p. 36)

References and Additional Readings

Ball, D. (1997). What do students know? Facing challenges of distance, context, and desire in trying to hear children. In T. Biddle, T. Good, & I. Goodson (Eds.), *International handbook on teachers and teaching* (pp. 769–817). Dordrecht, Netherlands: Kluwer Press.

Ballenger, C. (1999). *Teaching other people's children: Literacy and learning in a bilingual classroom.* New York: Teachers College Press.

Cochran-Smith, M. (1995a). Uncertain allies: Understanding the boundaries of race and teaching. *Harvard Educational Review, 63,* 541–570.

Cochran-Smith, M. (1995b). Color blindness and basket making are not the answers: Confronting the dilemmas of race, culture, and language diversity in teacher education. *American Educational Research Journal, 32,* 493–522.

Duckworth, E. (1996). *"The having of wonderful ideas" and other essays on teaching and learning.* New York: Teachers College Press.

Entwistle, D., and Alexander, K. (1989). Early schooling as a "critical period" phenomenon. In K. Namboodiri & R. Corwin (Eds.), *Research in Sociology of Education and Socialization,* Volume 8, (pp. 27–55) Greenwich, CT: Jai Press.

Heath, S. B. (1983). *Ways with words: Language, life, and work in communities and classrooms.* New York: Cambridge University Press.

Hiebert, J., Carpenter, T. P., Fennema, E., Fuson, K. C., Wearne, D., Murray, H., et al. (1997). *Making sense: Teaching and learning mathematics with understanding.* Portsmouth, NH: Heinemann.

Hudicourt-Barnes, J. (2003). The use of argumentation in Haitian Creole science classrooms. *Harvard Educational Review, 73*(1), 73–93.

King, J. (1991). Dysconscious racism: Ideology, identity, and the miseducation of teachers. *The Journal of Negro Education, 60,* 133–146.

Ladson-Billings, G. (1994). *The dreamkeepers: Successful teaching for African American students.* San Francisco: Jossey-Bass.

Ladson-Billings, G. (1995). Toward a theory of culturally relevant pedagogy. *American Educational Research Journal, 32,* 465–491.

Ladson-Billings, G. (2002). I ain't writin' nuttin': Permission to fail and demands to succeed in urban classrooms. In L. Delpit & J. K. Dowdy (Eds.), *The skin that we speak: Thoughts on language and culture in the classroom* (pp. 107–120). New York: The New Press.

Lawrence, S. M., & Tatum, B. D. (1997). White educators as allies: Moving from awareness to action. In M. Fine, L. Weis, L. C. Powell, & L. M. Wong (Eds.), *Off white: Readings on race, power, and society* (pp. 333–342). New York: Routledge.

Lewis, A. (2003). *Race in the schoolyard: Negotiating the color line in classrooms and communities.* New Brunswick, New Jersey and London: Rutgers University Press.

Moschkovich, J. (1999). Supporting the participation of English language learners in mathematical discussions. *For the Learning of Mathematics,* 19(1), 11–19.

National Council of Teachers of Mathematics. (2000). *Principles and standards for school mathematics.* Reston, VA: Author.

Obidah, J., & Teel, K. M. (1996). The impact of race on cultural differences on the teacher/student relationship: A collaborative classroom study by an African American and Caucasian teacher research team. *Kansas Association for Supervision and Curriculum Development Record,* 14, 70–86.

Obidah, J., & Teel, K. M. (2001). *Because of the kids.* New York: Teachers College Press.

Paley, V. G. (1989). *White teacher.* Cambridge, MA: Harvard University Press.

Schifter, D. (1996). *What's happening in math class? Vol. 1: Envisioning new practices through teacher narratives ; Vol. 2: Reconstructing professional identities.* New York: Teachers College Press.

Titles of Grade 3 Teacher Notes by Unit

Unit 1 Trading Stickers, Combining Coins

Place Value (U1: 143)
Stickers: A Context for Place Value (U1: 145)
Mathematical Representations for Addition and
    Subtraction (U1: 147)
Addition Strategies (U1: 149)
Does Order Matter in Addition? (U1: 152)
Assessment: Hundreds, Tens, and Ones (U1: 153)
Learning the Addition Combinations (U1: 159)
Assessment: Addition Combinations (U1: 161)
End-of-Unit Assessment (U1: 164)

Unit 2 Surveys and Line Plots

Choosing Questions for Data Collection (U2: 157)
About Categorical Data in This Unit (U2: 159)
Collecting Data from Other Classes (U2: 162)
About Numerical Data in This Unit (U2: 163)
Focusing on the Shape of the Data (U2: 164)
Data Terms (U2: 166)
Representing Numerical Data (U2: 168)
Finding and Using the Median (U2: 170)
Assessment: How Many People Live in Your
    Home? (U2: 171)
End-of-Unit Assessment (U2: 176)

Unit 3 Collections and Travel Stories

Place Value (U3: 191)
Mathematical Representations for Addition and
    Subtraction (U3: 193)
Addition Strategies (U3: 195)
Assessment: Addition Strategies (U3: 198)
Learning and Assessing Subtraction Facts Related to
    Addition Combinations up to 10 + 10 (U3: 202)
Types of Subtraction Situations (U3: 203)
Assessment: How Far Did They Travel? (U3: 205)
Subtraction Strategies (U3: 210)
End-of-Unit Assessment (U3: 212)

Unit 4 Perimeter, Angles, and Area

Metric and U.S. Standard Units of Measure (U4: 137)
Making Careful Measurements (U4: 138)
Introducing and Managing the *LogoPaths*
    Software (U4: 139)
About the Mathematics in the *LogoPaths*
    Software (U4: 142)
What's an -Omino (U4: 143)
Understanding the Area of Triangles (U4: 144)
Assessment: Make a Shape (U4: 145)
Beyond Vocabulary (U4: 148)
End-of-Unit Assessment (U4: 149)

Unit 5 Equal Groups

Images of Multiplication (U5: 145)
Representing Multiplication with the Number
    Line (U5: 147)
The Relationship Between Multiplication and
    Division (U5: 148)
Assessment: Solving Problems About Our
    Pictures (U5: 149)
Patterns in the Skip Counting Charts (U5: 152)
Students' Problems with Skip Counting (U5: 154)
Assessment: *Counting Around the Class* (U5: 155)
Representing Multiplication with Arrays (U5: 157)
Learning Multiplication Combinations (U5: 160)
Two Kinds of Division: Sharing and Grouping (U5: 163)
End-of-Unit Assessment (U5: 165)

Unit 6 Stories, Tables, and Graphs

Using Line Graphs to Represent Change (U6: 117)
Assessment: A Summer Day in Cairo, Egypt (U6: 119)
Repeating Patterns and Counting Numbers (U6: 124)
Students' Representations of Change (U6: 126)
Using and Interpreting Tables (U6: 128)
Graphs of Situations with a Constant Rate of
    Change (U6: 130)
End-of-Unit Assessment (U6: 134)

Unit 7 Finding Fair Shares

Why Are Fractions Difficult? Developing Meaning for
    Fractions (U7: 109)
Assessment: Sharing Four Brownies (U7: 111)
Visualizing Fraction Equivalencies (U7: 113)
End-of-Unit Assessment (U7: 115)

Unit 8 How Many Hundreds? How Many Miles?

Learning and Assessing Multiplication
    Combinations (U8: 149)
Addition Strategies (U8: 152)
Does Order Matter in Addition? (U8: 155)
Assessment: Addition Strategies (U8: 156)
Types of Subtraction Situations (U8: 160)
Learning and Assessing Subtraction Facts Related to
    Addition Combinations up to 10 + 10 (U8: 162)
Subtraction Strategies (U8: 163)
Assessment: Subtraction Strategies (U8: 165)
Reasoning and Proof in Mathematics (U8: 168)
End-of-Unit Assessment (U8: 171)

Unit 9 Solids and Boxes

Geometric Solids: Types and Terminology (U9: 95)
Strategies for Finding the Number of Cubes in
    a Box (U9: 96)
Assessment: Writing About How Many Cubes (U9: 97)
Strategies for Boxes That Hold 12 Cubes (U9: 100)
End-of-Unit Assessment (U9: 101)

PART 7

Working with the Range of Learners

Preview

All teachers are faced with the challenge of meeting the needs of a range of learners in their classrooms. The range of learners can include students who struggle in certain areas of mathematics, those who excel in math, students who are English Language Learners, and students who have particular learning needs.

This section contains a series of case studies written by third-grade teachers from urban, suburban, and rural schools, telling how they implemented the *Investigations* program in their classrooms. The students in these classrooms vary on many dimensions, including gender, language, culture and ethnicity, and special needs. They present a range of strengths and needs in their prior experience with mathematics and their confidence in the classroom.

Through their writing, these teachers bring us into their classrooms and invite us to participate in how they think about supporting their range of learners. As they captured moments in time in their classrooms, the teachers did not intend to provide exemplary actions to be emulated or a how-to manual of what to do for particular students or with particular activities. Rather, they offer the kind of thinking teachers do as a matter of course in their teaching. Through the hundreds of interactions they have with their students each day, teachers try to understand what those students bring to their learning and how to support them in moving further. In these case studies, they share some of that thinking.

We collected these cases together in this book, rather than including them with the curriculum units, because they are not designed to illustrate "how to do" a particular activity. Rather, as a group, they provide examples and questions to inspire your own questioning and reflection. You may want to use this set of cases on your own or discuss them with a group of colleagues.

Keep in mind that each case provides only a glimpse into a teacher's classroom. Just as you would not expect anyone to understand the complexity of the issues you face in your own classroom from such a brief glimpse, the cases cannot provide all the background information you might need to understand a particular teacher's decision with a particular student on a particular day. But you do not need to know more detail to use these cases for your own professional development. Use them as starting points when considering similar issues that you face with your students. The questions at the end of each case provide a starting point for discussion. If you discuss these cases with colleagues in a cross-grade group, you will have even more examples to consider by combining the sets of cases from two or more grades.

The classroom cases are grouped into three thematic sections, focusing on some of the most important issues teachers face as they work to meet the needs of their students. In the first section, "Setting Up the Mathematical Community," teachers write about how they create a supportive and productive learning environment in their classrooms. In the second section, "Accommodations for Learning," teachers focus on specific modifications they make to meet the needs of some of their learners. Because these teachers chose to write about particular students in their classrooms, the cases do not cover all the kinds of needs and accommodations you might encounter. However, even though the specific students discussed may differ from students in your own classroom, these teachers consistently found that accommodations they had made for one student often spilled over to benefit other students with related needs. In the last section, "Language and Representation," teachers share how they help students use representations and develop language to investigate and express mathematical ideas.

There is, of course, much overlap. Some cases illustrate ideas that could fall into more than one section. You will find ideas from one section cropping up in the cases in other sections. For example, when teachers develop accommodations for learning, they are often using mathematical representations or helping students connect their language to the mathematical ideas.

Note: Pseudonyms have been used for all student and teacher names.

Summary of Cases

Setting Up the Mathematical Community

Happy New School Year!

Tara Thompson shares the strategies she uses to encourage her students to participate in mathematical discussions.

Creating a Culture for Math Class

Jamie Emerson teaches her students how to give and receive constructive feedback so as to create a community of learners who are able to positively challenge each other's thinking.

The Value of "Disagreeing"

Kara Sawyer helps her students examine their own feelings about disagreeing and shows them how expressing disagreements and challenging one another's ideas can help expand the mathematical knowledge of all learners.

Student Grouping: Using the Demands of the Task to Shape the Groups

Kara Sawyer creates math groups by thinking about how her particular students can support each other's mathematical thinking.

Creating Effective Partnerships: Using Flexible Grouping to Enhance Learning

Lucy King shares how she creates and manages flexible groups to enhance learning.

Accommodations for Learning

The Case of Ezra Who "Just Knows" the Answer

Ezra is frustrated by math activities that require him to show his work. Katrina Sajak creates an accommodation that eases his tension and helps her think more deeply about when "showing work" is purposeful.

The Case of Julia: Supporting Participation in Math Discussions

Jamie Emerson shares how she helped one of her students participate in mathematical discussions.

The Case of Nan: Finding the Meaning of 7 × 5

Lucy King helps a student work through her confusion when writing a multiplication story problem.

The Case of Ellen: Deciding When to Nudge

Katrina Sajak helps a student develop a more efficient strategy for solving division problems.

The Case of Mary and Tamara: Shifting Understanding from One Third of a Discrete Whole to One Third of a Group

Tara Thompson works with two students as they attempt to create designs that are one third yellow.

Language and Representation

Count and Compare: An Extension to Support a Range of Learners

Katrina Sajak creates an extension to the game *Count and Compare* to maximize the use of arrays as a visual representation for multiplication and to address the diverse needs of the students in her classroom.

Using Representations in Brownie Problems: What Do You Call a Third of a Half?

Yukio struggles to share five brownies among three people. Lucy King helps him correctly represent and identify each person's fair share.

Setting Up the Mathematical Community

Happy New School Year!

Building a math community involves adults and students working together to create a culture that will enable each person to be productive and become excited about mathematics. In this case, Tara Thompson reflects on her goals for her students as they develop into a classroom community—in particular her goal of creating a safe environment "that encourages the students to be (or become) risk takers." Ms. Thompson recognizes that to take risks, students must feel safe about expressing their ideas about the mathematics they are working on.

I want my students to know that we *talk* about math. I want to help my students see the importance of discussions—of participating in discussions and valuing the ideas of their classmates. I try very hard to let them know that I am interested in their ideas and that questions are important. I ask students what they think all day long. I model listening intently, and I often restate what I hear them say to provide an example of ways to engage in productive conversations.

Here are some strategies I use to encourage participation.

1. I am always asking questions:

   "Does anyone want to tell us what you think the answer might be? Even if you're not sure or if it feels like a 'guess' right now, it's okay to take a chance and tell us your idea."

   As the year progresses, I want students to show how their ideas and solutions are based on evidence and reasoning. However, at the beginning of the year, I find that giving them permission to say what might feel to them like a "guess" frees up some students who would otherwise be reluctant to speak. Because many of these "guesses" are actually based on good mathematical thinking, I take the opportunity to point out how the idea or answer they expressed was based on what they knew.

2. After a discussion is underway, I ask if there is anyone who has not had a chance to say something out loud yet.

I tell them that I want everyone to have a chance to share their ideas.

3. Sometimes when many students have something to say, I ask the students to turn to their neighbors and share their ideas. Talking in pairs lets everyone have a chance to respond in a nonthreatening manner. It also serves as a kind of rehearsal by giving students a chance to try explaining their thinking to other students. They can practice clarifying their thinking in response to other students' reactions. In addition, I have an opportunity to eavesdrop on the conversations and identify ideas that can be shared with the whole class.

4. During discussions, I ask someone to say in his or her own words what he or she heard another student say. Asking for a restatement helps the students know that they should be listening, since I might ask for this at any time. In addition, restating can help to slow a discussion down when an important idea is shared that I want to make sure is really heard by all. If an idea cannot be restated, I ask the class if they would like to hear it again. This strategy is also useful when I'm not clear on a student's thinking! Hearing the idea explained by someone else can often clear it up for everyone.

5. We talk about the role of mistakes in our classroom and about being confused. I encourage students to think of mistakes as opportunities to learn something new. When I sense that confusion is in the air, I congratulate the class and tell them that they have found a really important idea: If it was a simple idea, we wouldn't be confused. I assure them that we'll work together to figure it out. We talk about what confusion feels like and how it feels to figure out something hard. It's important to acknowledge the negative feeling that confusion can bring. At the same time, helping students have a more positive emotional reaction to confusion can turn a situation that could be frustrating and unproductive into something challenging and productive.

Ms. Thompson begins the year aware that students enter her classroom with differing ideas, experiences, and fears related to participating in mathematical discussions. Through careful modeling of her own interest in their thinking and their questions, she helps her students learn to respond thoughtfully to each others' ideas. Through emphasizing that people's guesses can give us great new ideas to think about, that mistakes are opportunities to learn something new, and that confusion is an important part of learning, Ms. Thompson helps create a safe atmosphere for her students in which they can become risk takers in the mathematics classroom.

Questions for Discussion

1. **What are some of the issues Ms. Thompson considers as she works with her students to create a safe and productive mathematical community?**

2. **As the year begins, what ideas, experiences, and fears might your students have about expressing their mathematical ideas? In what ways do you allow students to talk about these issues?**

3. **What strategies do you use to encourage participation and risk taking in mathematical discussions?**

Creating a Culture for Math Class

As the school year begins, students and teachers work together to establish a classroom community that will enable each person to work productively and become excited about mathematics. One aspect of this work is establishing what it means to share ideas in a mathematics classroom. For many students, the risks involved in putting ideas forward to teachers and peers seem daunting.

Jamie Emerson knows that to create a successful math community with her students, she must build a safe environment in which students are willing to take risks and share their thoughts and ideas. Even though the students in Ms. Emerson's class arrive with diverse needs and a variety of mathematical experiences, she

recognizes that all of these students need support in learning how to share their ideas in the mathematics classroom. Here Ms. Emerson reflects on how she works with her students on these issues at the beginning of the year.

We talk about how to share our ideas with a focus on encouraging students to share their complete thinking, with an example to support it. For example, when a student says, "The answer is less than a $1.00," I always ask, "How do you know?" Sometimes, students who are not used to being asked to support their thinking interpret my question as a sign that their answer is incorrect. I talk to them about how explaining their thinking helps them to understand the mathematics more deeply and to work through areas that they may find confusing. It also lets me know what each student understands about the mathematics we are working on. When they understand my reasons for asking "How do you know?" they eventually begin providing this information themselves.

Sharing ideas means taking risks, and I let my students know that it is not okay to say to someone, "That's not the right answer!" We had a conversation about this topic the other day. It went like this:

Teacher: What if Sarah shares her answer and Sylvan disagrees with her? How can he let her know in a friendly, constructive way? Remember, we want to talk like mathematicians about our work.

Marlee: He could say, "I disagree with you."

Nicole: He could say, "I got a different answer."

Yash: He could ask, "How did you get your answer?"

Teacher: What do we think? Which ones could we write down on our poster to remind us of how we want to work together during math time?

For part of this conversation, we also talked about the importance of receiving feedback gracefully.

Teacher: So when Sylvan says to Sarah, "I disagree with you," how might Sarah feel?

Dorca: She might feel sad because she worked hard on her answer.

Alexa: She might feel upset or mad because sometimes it is hard for her to share.

We talked about the importance of remembering that our classmates' feedback is not about our ability to do math. Instead, it is about how our thinking is different from another person's, supporting each other in finding correct answers, and working through those areas in which we disagree.

"I disagree with you" is hard for students to hear, especially those who do not have confidence in their abilities as mathematicians, and especially when it is said by someone whom the class perceives as "smart." When these moments arise, I sometimes take time to focus on the receiver's feelings with the whole class. I want students to understand that disagreements can be handled in a way that facilitates our learning and that it is important for the whole class to work together to create a safe environment.

For students, sharing ideas in a mathematical discussion means taking the risk of being disagreed with by the teacher and peers. Disagreements are not inherently negative; rather, they can provide a place for in-depth conversations. Yet, Ms. Emerson recognizes how difficult disagreements are for many students. As a result, she structures class discussions that allow students to express their fears while learning how to give and receive constructive feedback. By stressing that feedback is not about a student's ability to do math, Ms. Emerson helps students gradually understand the positive aspect of disagreement in mathematical discussions while giving them the tools they need to work through those times in which they disagree.

Questions for Discussion

1. What apprehensions might your students have about taking risks in mathematical discussions? What steps did Ms. Emerson take to help her students work through their apprehensions?

2. How do you help your students learn to give and receive constructive feedback? How do you help them learn to handle disagreements in a way that facilitates learning?

The Value of "Disagreeing"

As the school year begins, Kara Sawyer works hard to establish a community of learners in her classroom by establishing a set of values for this community. Ms. Sawyer recognizes that these values must be modeled and learned. She also recognizes that students may enter her classroom with different sets of beliefs and experiences about what some of these values imply.

I want students to understand about how we will learn together and the kinds of responsibilities such a vision requires for each member of the "community." These responsibilities include the following:

- Revising and refining our ideas

- Building on each others' ideas

- Recognizing the value of disagreement

- Becoming "learning listeners," which means listening to understand, not just to be polite

- Taking responsibility for one's own learning

- Paying attention to a partner's needs and right to learn

- Growing and developing ideas *together*

A math class offers an important venue for highlighting these responsibilities and practicing them explicitly. An example from a math class at the beginning of the school year illustrates a way in which the class worked on developing an understanding of the "value of disagreement."

There is much that students have to figure out about the complexities of working together to enjoy the advantages that can be gained from working with others. In small groups, we had just played the game *Capture 5*. Because the group work context was fairly new to many of my students and because there were some problems that surfaced within some of the groups, I wanted to hear their reactions and responses. Therefore, I asked my students to write in their math journals about what went well and what didn't go well in the day's math class.

When I read their journal responses that night, I noticed that many students thought that successful group work meant that people agreed with each other. Here are some of the things they wrote: "It all went really well. We all agreed." and "We didn't have any disagreements." In contrast, one student wrote, "We didn't agree at first, but then we worked it out." I decided to use this as an opportunity to highlight the difference between two types of disagreements: those in which people fight and those in which they disagree and work through their disagreements. I also wanted to help students understand that learning benefits can come from the second type of disagreement.

Before our math class the next day, I copied some of the journal comments onto chart paper without identifying the authors of the comments. We started with the most common type that equated a good math session with everyone agreeing. Then I stated:

I know it can feel very nice and comfortable to be in a group where everyone agrees, but the last comment on this chart really caught my attention, and I want us to talk about it.

I directed their attention to the comment "We didn't agree at first, but then we worked it out" and asked if they knew the difference between fighting over different ideas and disagreeing and working through those disagreements together. Many hands went up, so I asked two volunteers to do a quick demonstration of the first kind of disagreement, using *Capture 5* as the example. They improvised beautifully!

Student 1: I landed on 75. That means I have 5 markers and you only have 4. I win!

Student 2: (interrupting) Nooooo! You're wrong! You can't land on 75 with those cards. You landed on 74, so you don't get a marker.

Student 1: (interrupting) Nope. I'm right!

The bickering went on for a few more rounds (much to the audience's delight) before I began the debriefing. I asked them how they would describe what happens when people argue this way. The students' responses included the following:

They're being close-minded.

They're so loud; they disturb other people.

They don't listen to each other.

From the many volunteers, I carefully selected two students to demonstrate to the class what the second type of disagreement looks like. We used the context of the coin card game *Who Has More?* This demonstration was very different from the first. Each student listened to and responded to the other's ideas. They used our class way of disagreeing by saying, "I have a different idea. Let's try your way first and then mine and we'll see if we get the same answer."

The other students immediately noticed the key differences and expressed that these partners were "open-minded learners" who were civil and calm as they listened to understand each other's ideas. The impact of the demonstration was profound. The students could clearly see how fighting over different ideas gets you nowhere, while working through disagreements contributes strongly to learning new things.

Throughout the year, I hope we have many disagreements about the ideas we are discussing and developing in our math sessions. It is through these disagreements that our ideas are challenged and our learning is expanded. For our community of learners to benefit from the variety of ideas that we have, the classroom needs to be a safe place for sharing these ideas respectfully. I want my students to know that in our classroom, respecting the ideas of others isn't just about agreeing with each other. It also has to be about challenging ideas when we don't agree.

For many students, "disagreeing" has a negative connotation. In some households and communities, disagreeing, particularly with an adult, is considered rude and disrespectful. Countering the negative connotations of argument is an important part of establishing a mathematical community in the classroom. Ms. Sawyer helped her students recognize that expressing disagreements and challenging ideas are crucial elements in expanding the mathematical knowledge of all learners.

Questions for Discussion

1. Ms. Sawyer recognized that students' attitudes about disagreement could present an obstacle to the types of discussions she hoped for in the mathematics classroom. How was she able to get the solution to this "problem" to come from the students rather than from the teacher?

2. What attitudes about disagreeing might your students bring with them to the classroom?

3. How can you respect students' cultural norms while helping them recognize and utilize disagreements as opportunities for learning?

Student Grouping: Using the Demands of the Task to Shape the Groups

Student grouping for mathematics instruction is an area that has received widespread attention in recent years. Some educators believe that homogeneous (ability) grouping is a way to ensure that students obtain the specific experiences and skills needed to move their thinking forward. Others feel that heterogeneous grouping offers students a chance to share their thinking across ability levels, leading to increased understanding of concepts and topics for all students. In either case, educators must consider the intersection of mathematical content, student ability, and experiences when grouping students for mathematics activities and instruction. They think flexibly about student grouping, according to the demands of the task.

Kara Sawyer describes her thinking about student grouping for an investigation that involved describing and representing categorical data. Ms. Sawyer bases her decisions on the unique mathematical and social contributions, personalities, and dispositions of her students.

How should I organize students for a categorical data activity? There were many things to consider. I decided to focus on issues that are more related to students' learning styles rather than on their math ability level. I identified the following criteria in determining how I would partner students: organization, ability to compromise, and response to ambiguity.

- *Organization:* Because there is a high demand to keep pieces of data organized and accounted for throughout the categorical data activity, I wanted at least one of the partners to be a student who had some ease in this regard. I could have paired students of similar organizational skills together, but I didn't think that such a structure would have been as productive for this first experience with categorical data.

- *Ability to Compromise:* I also knew that one aspect of the intellectual demand of this work was the ability to consider multiple arrangements of the data. This would involve a lot of negotiation and listening to each other's ideas. As I created the pairs, I decided to have some mixed pairing and some similar pairings with regard to this criterion.

In most pairs, one partner was the kind of student who engaged easily in compromise, while the other partner struggled more with it. In a few pairings, I matched students who struggled together, knowing that I would need to provide support for them to finish the task.

- *Response to Ambiguity:* Working with categorical data is often an intellectually "messy" activity. Because there are few absolutes, students have to make decisions that cannot be predetermined by the directions for the task. As I considered partnering my students, I thought about how they dealt with ambiguity. A few of them had a low tolerance for anything that wasn't spelled out and readily apparent. As a result, they would become uneasy if there was more than one answer. I decided to mostly pair students who had similar levels of tolerance for ambiguity, and, in so doing, I was committing myself to working with the students for whom this task would be more difficult.

I created partners based mostly on these three criteria; but, of course, there were a few other considerations: Who had the potential for silliness with each other? Who had particular difficulty engaging with partners? Who needed support to assert their ideas? Who needed to be pushed out of their comfort zones?

As I observed the students working together, I could see which pairings were successful and which were not; there were a few surprises, both good and not so good. Which factors had I anticipated and created on purpose? Which ones had I missed? As I enter into my second round of grouping for the next categorical data activity in the curriculum unit, I will have to take stock of what happened during this activity and decide how I will use this information to create the next grouping situation. Would it be beneficial to keep partner pairs intact, or should they be changed? Should students form their own partners? Will they work in small groups rather than in pairs? There are many questions for me to consider throughout the school year.

Cooperative grouping in mathematics is an important strategy for enhancing learning. Yet, math groups are often formed without careful attention to the ways in which students might support each other's mathematical thinking. In this case, Ms. Sawyer explores the ways that she pairs students and the reasons behind these actions. Ms. Sawyer describes an important next step in meeting the needs of her students through her continued thinking about the future grouping of students based on information gathered from this experience.

Questions for Discussion

1. What aspects of both students and the math activity does Ms. Sawyer consider when she is deciding how best to support her students in their work together?

2. In what ways do you think about grouping students as you plan your math instruction?

3. What are ways Ms. Sawyer or you might keep track of groupings and how successful are they?

Creating Effective Partnerships: Using Flexible Grouping to Enhance Learning

Lucy King recognizes that having students work with partners or in small groups encourages them to deepen their understanding of mathematics as they share their ideas with other students. Ms. King is deliberate in how she assigns the groupings in her classroom.

Developing the skills needed to work with others is an important life skill, but it also has academic benefits. In my classes each year, I have a variety of reasons for grouping my students, including the following:

- *Working with others promotes discussion.* It is much easier to encourage students to talk about their thinking in a large group when they first have someone to talk to in a small group or pair.

- *Listening to the students talk to each other often gives me more information than I would get from individual questioning.* As I walk around and listen to my students talking to their partners or in small groups, I get a sense of what they understand and what they need to work on. I am able to join right in with their discussions when I know they will benefit from my attention.

- *When students work in groups, I can check in with more students during one class.* Each time I stop, I have the opportunity to check in with two or more students at once.

- *I can make choices about who will work effectively together based on my knowledge of the social and mathematical strengths of individual students and those areas in which they need support and development.* I can then form and change groupings based on the mathematics and the needs of the individual students involved. For example, at times I choose to place students with similar levels of understanding together so that they can work on problems without one student simply telling the others the answers. Then, after solving problems in pairs or small groups, two pairs or groups of students can meet together to share their solutions and be exposed to other ways of approaching the mathematics. These meetings can be across ability levels. Other times, I pair students because they bring very different strengths and/or challenges to the pair that could be complementary and move both students forward.

Students often want to choose their own partners, and I make sure to provide students with some opportunities to form their own partnerships. However, they usually work with the partners I have assigned. Assigning partners and helping them learn to work together productively helps to resolve many of the social issues that would otherwise arise, particularly early in the year.

To create effective partnerships, I need to get to know my students and their abilities and attitudes about math. To do this, I give students a variety of problems to solve during the first few days of school, being sure to include problems that have several possible answers. For example,

Henry had a birthday party. He counted 24 legs at the party. His friends were butterflies, pigs, and ducks. How many creatures were at the party?

I choose a problem such as this for a number of reasons.

- It is accessible and engaging to all students. Everyone can find an answer.

- No one "knows" the answer before they start the problem.

- Trying to find all the answers keeps the students engaged for a long period of time, allowing me the opportunity to get around to all the tables to observe how students are approaching the problem. This gives me a sense of the math skills of different students.

After assigning other open-ended questions during the first few days of school, I have enough sense of my students and their strengths and needs that I can assign partners effectively.

As students start working together, I look for examples of "good working together" behaviors that I can point out to the class. In addition, we take the time during math class to talk about how pairs and groups are working. We resolve any issues and create a class definition of "good partners" that we post and refer to throughout the year.

I aim to change partnerships about once a month, as students' understandings change and develop throughout the year and as we move through the various topics in the math curriculum. The groupings I form for geometry or fractions often look quite different from those I form while studying numbers and operations.

I used to drive myself crazy trying to form new partnerships and keep track of them. I spent too much time and still managed to put students together who had already been partners. Several years ago, a colleague shared a way of managing all of these groupings. I now make an index card for each student in my room, listing all of the different categories of partnerships: math, spelling, computer, and so forth. Each time I make new partners, I label the two students' cards with the same number. When I need to form new groups, I can see from the students' cards which students have been partners before. I also keep a master card with each of the categories where I list the dates each of the groups was formed, allowing me to see how long students have been partnered together.

Because of the benefits for my students and myself, making groups work well is well worth the effort.

Cooperative grouping in mathematics can be an important strategy in enhancing learning, but all too often cooperative groups are formed without careful attention to the ways in which students might support each other's mathematical thinking. Grouping is sometimes done strictly according to mathematical ability or to create an arbitrary mix of students in terms of gender, race and ethnicity, and language preference. Sometimes, groups are self-chosen, so that many students consistently work with the same individuals.

Ms. King illustrates a more complex way of thinking about student groupings that takes into consideration students' mathematical abilities, as well as their personalities and her own mathematical goals for each student. Ms. King makes her expectations clear for students, reviews the purpose of the partnerships, provides regular check-ins, and alters pairings when they appear not to meet her expectations.

Encouraging students to work together provides opportunities for students to expand their mathematical knowledge and contribute to the social climate of the classroom. Students need numerous opportunities to work in a variety of thoughtfully chosen groupings.

Questions for Discussion

1. What are the benefits that Ms. King believes she and her students receive by using flexible grouping?

2. How does she maintain and manage the groups she creates throughout the school year?

3. In what ways can you enhance the success of particular students in your classroom through flexible grouping?

4. In what ways do you make your decisions about grouping explicit for students?

Accommodations for Learning

The Case of Ezra Who "Just Knows" the Answer

Motivating students to become meaningfully engaged with the work is an ongoing concern for all teachers. But while the issue of motivation is significant in working with all learners, it can take a surprisingly central role in our work with those students who arrive at the answers quickly and are constantly seeking additional challenge. In the following case, Katrina Sajak works with Ezra as she identifies ways to redefine her expectations for him. In doing so, Ms. Sajak is able to meet her math goals not only for Ezra but also for other students in her class.

Every year I have at least one student in my class like Ezra. He is one of those quick-thinking human-calculator kids who "just knows" the answer. He is not an arithmetic-only student who knows only a narrow slice of the mathematical ideas being studied. He has some good, solid understanding about numbers and operations, and he enjoys playing around with mathematical ideas. What frustrates Ezra is the requirement that he "show his thinking" or "show how he solved the problem."

The kind of math work we do in our class demands that students learn how to effectively communicate, model, and represent their thinking so that each student becomes able to work with each other's ideas. I value the way in which these representations help students deepen their own understandings and promote discourse in our classroom community, and I am committed to helping all students achieve this goal.

For many students, showing how they solved the problem is easy because as they are solving it, they leave behind a record of their solution. Students like Ezra "just know," and they hear the requirement to show their thinking as a burden—an extra step they have to do. As the year progresses, these students can become deflated, confrontational, and defensive if we continue to require them to carry out these extra steps. With this in mind, I decided to find out more about what was going on for Ezra. An opportunity came up as the class was working on *How Many More?* story problems. Students were asked to solve each problem and show the solution with an equation and a number line.

When I first looked at Ezra's paper, I struggled to figure out what to say to him about it. Although he got five of the six problems correct, he had completely avoided using the number line, and the steps of his solutions were poorly organized on the page. I knew it was time to talk with him about communicating his thinking. I needed him to see the value in this aspect of learning mathematics! In addition, I was worried about the problem he got wrong (he had written $43 + 18 = 68$); Ezra calculates problems like this all the time in his head—just for fun!

As I began to talk to him about his work, I immediately felt his distress. Ezra was not comfortable, nor was he familiar, with being "unsuccessful" in math. He said, "I have a really hard time with stuff like this. I know the answer right away, and then when I have to go back and count tens and stuff and put it on a number line, I get all confused and mess up!" He was trying so hard to meet the expectations of the assignment, yet it was inconsistent with how he worked.

I asked him if he thought it would help to just write down the answer as soon as he got it. Then he wouldn't have to hold on to it while he was showing his solution. He looked somewhat relieved, but there was still something bothering him about the "show" part.

I decided to give Ezra a slightly different direction—to satisfy his way of working as well as my need for students to represent their ideas. Instead of having him "show his thinking," or "show his work," I asked Ezra to "show why the answer makes sense." Basically, I asked him to prove why the answer he got is a reasonable and accurate one for the problem. It seems like such a minor revision, but for Ezra, the effect was profound. His expression lightened, he smiled, and he hugged me! As he returned to his work, he had renewed energy and a much livelier engagement with the activity. He has sustained that energy and engagement for several weeks now.

This case demonstrates how a carefully considered, seemingly simple extension can have far-reaching results. In resolving her dilemma with Ezra, Ms. Sajak begins by reflecting on her objectives for the activity. She clarifies for herself the importance of asking students to represent their mathematical thinking: It helps individuals think more deeply about the problem while also providing a vehicle for students to talk with one another about their work. However, when students naturally skip the recording of steps that they easily understand for problems they can solve easily, it can be tedious and unproductive for them to go back to do additional recording.

Ms. Sajak then applies some creative problem solving, working with Ezra to arrive at an agreement that satisfies her goals but is more consistent with his approach to learning. Ultimately, Ezra is able to complete the assignment and create a representation that he can share with others. Perhaps even more importantly, Ms. Sajak's solution enables Ezra to see the value in looking at the big ideas behind his answers and to maintain his enthusiasm about learning mathematics.

Questions for Discussion

1. Ms. Sajak considered Ezra's strengths, along with her own math goals for him, to create a more challenging mathematical activity for Ezra. What factors did Ms. Sajak consider when creating an accommodation for Ezra?

2. Why did Ms. Sajak feel that it was important for Ezra to represent his mathematical ideas and solutions? Do you agree with her thoughts on this subject? How do you make decisions about when it is productive for students to "show their work" or explain how they solved a problem?

3. Have you had students like Ezra who "just know" the answers but struggle with representing their work? How do you help them understand the value of representations in deepening their own mathematical thinking while bringing their ideas to the rest of the class?

The Case of Julia: Supporting Participation in Math Discussions

Participation in math discussions encourages students to communicate their thinking, reflect on their knowledge, and make sense of other students' understandings. In the process, students are able to deepen their own mathematical understanding.

Although it is important for all students to build communication skills, participation does not always come easily. In the following case, Jamie Emerson shares her approach to helping Julia, a struggling math student, participate in math discussions.

Julia does not talk much in class in any subject, but she particularly shuts down in math. She is a hard worker, is an average reader, has a few close friends, and generally seems connected to the students around her. When asked to respond to a question, she will often shake her head and look around at anyone other than the teacher, unless she is in a small group. Even then, she must be encouraged to participate verbally. Last year Julia struggled with math but never gave up. This year her difficulties continue. She feels insecure and therefore prefers not to participate.

In a classroom with a wide range of learners, it is important to find ways to bring all students into the discussions and to value each answer or offering. Over these first months of class, the students and I have worked through the need for everyone to feel it is safe to make mistakes. I pay attention to the way in which I respond to students' ideas and strategies and encourage each student to find the relevance in each other's responses, instead of focusing on what is "wrong" about the solution. Within this context, my focus with Julia is to create and maintain an environment that supports her where she is and allows and encourages her to share her thinking in whole class discussions. I expect that everyone will participate in math discussions.

After her initial reflection on Julia's difficulties in participating in conversations, Ms. Emerson planned a variety of ways to encourage Julia to practice exchanging and sharing ideas. Her goal is for Julia to gain confidence in her ability to participate, even if she makes mistakes.

Having Julia work in pairs has helped at times, especially if she has a partner who can listen to and mirror what she is saying. Working in small groups and having more exposure to talking about math concepts has also helped Julia. I have to think carefully about who her partners are.

As for her participation in the large group, I have let Julia know beforehand that I will call on her to answer a particular question. Sometimes that means setting it up before the group meets and sometimes it means calling on students with hands raised and then letting Julia know that I want input from her next. She has responded well to this encouragement.

These interventions seem to have helped. Lately, Julia has gathered some momentum! She is participating a bit more in discussions and is offering answers herself, without my calling on her first. Her answers remain tentative but mostly correct. I'm not sure what is helping her—whether it is the extra conversations, or the fact that she is just ready to get the math more easily, or both—but she is better able to continue on her own once she has started.

As for me, I am still working on how to respond to each student's contribution to the math discussion, especially in those situations where the student's contribution is only partially right or completely incorrect. For students like Julia, their ability to feel good and confident about the math they are doing is directly related to their ability to communicate about their work—what they understand as well as what they are confused about. Like it or not, much of what a student says and how the teacher responds affects how that student is perceived within the math classroom: Are they smart, dumb, or someone you want for a partner? I want to make sure that I find ways to value each student's contribution so that the group will value the student as well.

As Ms. Emerson thinks about ways to help Julia, she also reflects on the impact her own actions have in building confidence among her students. She realizes that creating an inclusive environment in which students participate in discussions takes a lot of thinking and planning on the part of the teacher. It involves considering the students' strengths and weaknesses as well as her own behavior and its influence.

Questions for Discussion

1. What were Ms. Emerson's strategies for encouraging Julia's participation in the mathematics community, both in small groups and in whole class discussions?

2. What do you do to bring into the conversation students who usually prefer not to participate?

3. How do you respond to students' comments so that they are willing to communicate their ideas, even though they might be incorrect?

The Case of Nan: Finding the Meaning of 7 × 5

Lucy King has particular concerns for those students in her class who need extra support to become successful learners. Nan is one of those students. Throughout the year, Ms. King has made modifications for Nan to make math activities more accessible to her. These include breaking tasks into smaller chunks, asking questions to clarify tasks and build on Nan's understanding, and having her restate problems in her own words. In this case, Ms. King writes about an exchange with Nan while students are working on problems for the class multiplication and division book.

Nan seemed to be having some difficulty getting started, so I suggested that she write a story problem to go with the expression 7×5. After letting her work on this for a while, I went back to see how she was doing. I noticed that Nan had written the following problem on her paper:

There were seven dogs and five people. How many dogs does each person get?

I asked her to read the problem to me, hoping that she'd notice that the action in her problem wasn't multiplication. No such luck. I then asked her to solve her problem for me. She happily counted out seven cubes and then put five new cubes out on her desk to "be the people." She dealt out the seven dogs and was not bothered as she told me, "These five people would get only one dog each."

I decided to spend some time with Nan, since it was clear that she needed help connecting her prior experiences and understandings to the new task before her. I knew she had good ideas, and I wondered what I could do to help her access these ideas on her own. For example, earlier in the unit, Nan had successfully drawn pictures of "things that come in groups" and had written sentences and equations to represent how many groups, how many in each group, and how many in all. She had shown many times that she could count by groups, connect skip counting to multiplication, model the action of the operation, and explain the meaning of the notation. But she needed to be able to access her knowledge independently and use it without me there to support her. Although Nan has shown significant progress this year in her mathematical understanding and has developed a growing sense of independence, I know she can still start down a path of thinking that leads to errors and confusion.

Teacher: What does 7×5 mean?

Nan: Seven groups of five.

Teacher: Great. Can you tell me how your problem fits seven groups of five?

Nan (smiling): It doesn't.

Teacher: So what can we do?

Nan: Um . . . I could use the cubes.

Teacher: Great.

Nan: Seven people and they have five dogs.

Although I assumed she was thinking about each person having five dogs, she wasn't. She seemed stuck and unable to proceed as she moved her cubes and talked to herself about "people and dogs, people. . . ." I wondered if she was having a difficult time paying attention to the idea of equal groups with this context of people and dogs.

Teacher: I wonder, Nan, if dogs and people are making this problem confusing for you. Do you remember when we all drew pictures of multiplication situations about 3 weeks ago?

Nan: Yes, we drew a lot.

Teacher: How about if you change the dogs to cookies?

I thought this might help her to think about counting by groups without my telling her that she was supposed to be paying attention to groups. Nan liked the idea.

Nan (smiling): Yeah, I could put the cookies in packs.

Teacher: Packs of what?

Nan: Packs of five. Then I would have seven bags.

Teacher: Sounds like a great problem. Can you write it on your paper?

Nan got right to work. I knew this task was not too difficult for her. I felt good about having asked her questions that scaffolded her thinking and moved her from her "stuck" place. I was able to help her use what she knows and build on work that she's done successfully in the past. My challenge for the rest of the year is to get Nan to a place where she can do these things for herself.

Nan has made significant progress over the course of the year and now works successfully with teacher support. In this example, Ms. King helped Nan use her knowledge of multiplication and the work she had done writing story problems in the past to correctly write a problem for 7×5. Her focus as the year goes on will be to give Nan the skills and confidence she needs to work more independently.

Questions for Discussion

1. What did Nan seem to know about multiplication and what confusions did she show? What questions did Ms. King ask that helped Nan think through the problem?

2. What are the next steps that Ms. King can take to help Nan move toward greater independence?

3. Do you have a student like Nan? What accommodations have you made to address that student's needs?

The Case of Ellen: Deciding When to Nudge

Katrina Sajak, like many teachers, strives to help move students forward with their mathematical thinking but often grapples with when to explicitly show students a particular strategy and when to let them work at their own pace. In this case, Ms. Sajak reflects on the decision she made to help Ellen develop a more efficient strategy for solving division story problems.

Every year as I get to know the students in my class, I typically face the decision about when to nudge them and when to let them work at the place they are. As I observe the way they learn and the way they approach mathematics, along with the skills and attitudes they bring, I also notice their confidence and tolerance for challenge. Some students are rather courageous and love as much challenge as possible. Others are reluctant, and some of those students bring with them the anxiety and insecurities of past experiences. Ellen was one such student.

Because I knew she needed a gentle touch, I began the year by treading lightly. After watching her for several weeks, I began to develop insights about Ellen as a learner. She rarely volunteered during math discussions, preferred not to be noticed during math work times, and claimed she did not like math and was terrible at doing it. I could see she had some glitches in her understanding of the number system.

She wasn't yet reliably using tens, and she had difficulty crossing the threshold of 100. Once in the 100s, though, she could manage pretty well until 200. Yet, Ellen also had some obvious strengths. It was hard for me to completely know what kind of support would help her most; but I knew whatever it was, it would have to start from a place of trust and understanding.

By November, things were moving along pretty well for Ellen in mathematics. She trusted herself more and also trusted that my confidence in her as a math student was genuine. She was gaining confidence and had a sense of herself as being competent to do math. Although very hardworking and industrious, she could still be a bit reluctant when she sensed that the ideas were advancing faster than she wanted. Despite her protests, she continued keeping pace and making progress. She was even surprising herself. It was in this mode that I knew I could again challenge her comfort level, as I had at other points during the first semester.

My students had authored division story problems for the class multiplication and division book and were solving each other's problems. I watched carefully as Ellen began. When the numbers were in a range that were workable or the numbers were "friendly" (such as $15 \div 5$ or $6 \div 2$), she was able to work confidently and with more efficiency. However, as soon as the numbers got slightly bigger or less familiar to her (splitting 18 muffins equally among 3 friends), she went back to making unbundled tally marks.

Earlier in the year, tally marks were her preferred strategy. In addition and subtraction she had moved on to greater efficiency. The number line work we did with those operations helped her make the leap to using multiples of 10. Now, however, with these less familiar operations, she was again less certain. For some students who need to make tally marks, I might have tried some other intervention to move them to greater efficiency; but with Ellen I felt confident that she knew more than she was accessing. I approached her desk with a plan. She was working on the following problem:

Ken has 52 toy trucks. He wants to invite 3 friends to his house to play with him and the trucks. For Ken and his friends to each get an equal number of trucks, how many trucks should each child get?

Ellen had written the equation $52 \div \underline{\quad} = 4$ for the problem and had drawn all 52 tally marks. She was beginning to circle them in groups of 12, starting from right to left. When I came over to her desk, she had already started erasing some of the circles, indicating that she knew there would be some extras left over after she circled the last 12. She told me she just guessed at 12 but that wouldn't work. Ellen had developed such a good sense about numbers, though, that her guess was so close. Unfortunately, she couldn't see it.

Teacher: Ellen, I am noticing that you are using those tally marks again. How's it working for you?

Ellen: Okay, except these numbers are too big for me. Sometimes I miscount them or erase them. Then I have to start all over again!

Here was my opening.

Teacher: Well, I think you know more about these numbers than you think. I'm going to take a chance with you right now and push you into something that I know you are ready for. You know that if I thought you needed to do it with tally marks, I would let you go on with it this way. But I'm not going to let you do that. I'm going to write an equation that I think you can use to solve this problem.

I wrote $4 \times 10 = \underline{\quad}$ on her paper. She immediately told me the answer was 40. I acknowledged that I thought she knew some things about multiples of 10 that could help her solve problems like this. I asked her if she could make use of that to solve the problem. She said she wasn't sure. I decided to help her reinterpret the problem.

Teacher: Well, suppose there were only 40 trucks. How many would each of the 4 friends get then?

Ellen: 10.

Teacher: Then, how many more would you have to work with if there were 52 trucks to begin with?

Ellen: Let's see. There would be 12 more, so it would be . . . 3 fours, so each child would get 3 more. That would be 10 and 3, or 13. (She wrote 13 in the blank to complete the equation.)

$$52 \div \underline{\ 13\ } = 4$$

Ellen had even surprised me with her ease in figuring this out so easily. I knew I had been leading her a lot, so after a short "debriefing" about the strategy I was suggesting, I left her to see if she could make use of it on her own.

The next day I checked back in with her.

Teacher: How are you doing with those problems, Ellen?

Ellen: They're really hard for me.

Teacher: Did that strategy work very well for you?

Ellen: Not really, I am pretty stuck.

Teacher: Let's take a look.

Sam was having a birthday party, and he was inviting 7 people to the party. He had 42 things for goody-bags. How many things will each child get?

$$42 \div \underline{\quad} = 7$$
$$10 \quad 10 \quad 10 \quad 10 \quad 2$$

It was at this point that I realized what had happened. Her work on this problem showed her first attempt, but she could not go any further. I realized that using 10s would, of course, only work when the product was equal to or greater than the known factor × 10. Giving 10 each to 7 people would equal 70 things, way more than the 42 things that Sam had for the goody-bags. Because I had made the strategy about 10s, I had failed to help Ellen think more generally in terms of using the biggest chunk she could manage times the known factor and then see how the leftovers could be divided up by that factor.

I decided to move to the next problem.

Tom, Paul, and Joe have to split a deck of 120 cards. How many cards do they each get? Equation: _____

I asked her to write the equation, using the missing factor notation this time instead of the division sign. She wrote

$$\underline{\hspace{2cm}} \times 3 = 120$$

Then I asked her to say the problem in her own words and to tell me what picture she had in her head for what was happening in the problem. Satisfied that she was ready to move to a solution, I asked her to make three circles to represent each person's share of the cards. She labeled each circle with the first initial of one of the people. I asked her to say the biggest number of cards she thought she could deal out to each. Her first guess was 40, and I asked her to write that number (not tally marks!) in each circle. When I asked her what she wanted to do next, she added 40 + 40 = 80, 80 + 20 = 100, 100 + 20 = 120; then she gasped, recognizing that she had figured it out! The figure below shows her final work.

Equation: 40 × 3 = 120

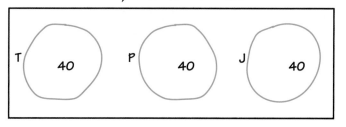

I decided to keep going. We proceeded similarly for the next problem.

Emma got 48 pieces of gum. Two friends came over. Emma wanted to share it with her friends. How many pieces would each person get?

I decided to comment only when she asked for it, when I was confused about something she did, or when I wanted to hear how she would explain the move she made. The only time I intervened was after she finished dealing out the first three 10s, and she thought she should try for another 10 for each friend. When she said she knew that would be too much, I asked if there was another chunk she would be able to use easily. From that point on, she worked independently toward the solution shown here:

Equation: 16 × 3 = 48

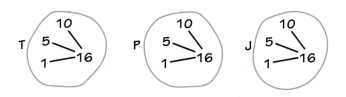

The next problem would be a real test of how confidently and competently Ellen would be able to make use of the strategy.

Sara is collecting cans and bottles for her community service project. She already has 27 cans and bottles, and she is putting them into 3 bags. How many will be in each bag?

Ellen started out by putting 12 cans or bottles in each bag, but after 2 bags, she stopped herself, and immediately went to putting just 5 into each bag. She did the problem completely on her own and felt successful continuing with the remaining problems.

Equation: $9 \times 3 = 27$

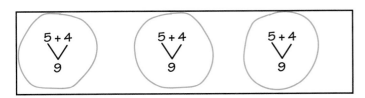

For Ellen, the nudging worked! It always feels like such a risk for me as the teacher to ascertain when there is an opening for me to intervene in this way. I felt that, for this student at this time, the nudge was necessary and well timed. I regret that my first attempt misled her, but I was grateful that she was open to returning to it again a few days later.

One thing I continue to learn is to trust the student. If I have misjudged what Ellen is ready for, she will not be able to make use of it, and ultimately that is what matters most. I have also learned how to read the student's reaction to my nudging. If I have moved Ellen too quickly from comfort to challenge, she may need more support working through ideas for herself at the place where she is comfortable before I can intervene with the next steps.

Ms. Sajak recognized that Ellen had strengths as a math learner, but she was anxious about math. She initially focused on observing Ellen's learning style and establishing a trusting relationship with her. She noted Ellen's progress as she learned to use multiples of 10 to solve addition and subtraction problems during the class work with the number line.

Later in the year, when Ms. Sajak noticed that Ellen was becoming frustrated as she attempted to use tally marks to solve multiplication and division problems, she decided to intervene and explicitly teach Ellen a more efficient strategy based on what Ellen understood about number relationships. This was a thoughtful decision on Ms. Sajak's part and was made only after determining that Ellen's understanding of equal groups and multiples would allow her to make sense of a new approach. Ms. Sajak modeled the strategy and worked with Ellen in her first attempts putting it into practice. Together they were able to work through the initial struggles of incorporating a new strategy.

Questions for Discussion

1. What strengths did Ellen show through her initial approach to the story problems?

2. How did these strengths and other information about Ellen help Ms. Sajak determine that Ellen might be ready to learn a more efficient approach?

3. What next steps would you take to move Ellen (or students like her) toward greater efficiency in solving division problems?

4. In this case, Ms. Sajak questions when to push a student to help him or her grow mathematically. How do you make these types of decisions in your classroom?

The Case of Mary and Tamara: Shifting Understanding from One Third of a Discrete Whole to One Third of a Group

The students in Tara Thompson's class have been working on the activity Half Yellow *in the unit* Finding Fair Shares. *In prior activities in this unit, fractions are considered in relationship to one whole object, for example, one brownie or one hexagon cookie. As Ms. Thompson writes, "Before encountering* Half Yellow, *one half is one of two equal pieces of a brownie or the red trapezoid in a fraction cookie." In this activity, students' ideas about what half means are stretched. Students now must shift their view of what the whole is as they construct different combinations of pattern block shapes. As the "whole" changes to a group of pattern blocks instead of a single hexagon, students' ideas about "half" must also change. In this case, Ms. Thompson writes about her interactions with two students, Mary and Tamara, who have worked through this confusion and successfully made designs that are half yellow. When Ms. Thompson suggests they try the extension,* One Third Yellow, *they are once again challenged to shift their thinking.*

Mary

Mary is a student with significant processing issues. It is difficult for her to make sense of and use language, especially when dealing with new or complex ideas. However, she has enjoyed the fraction work immensely. I think the visual nature of the activities has worked for her, and she has really been able to shine. She was excited when I suggested she make a design that was one third yellow.

When I approached Mary, she was finishing up coloring and labeling her design on paper. She had made a symmetrical design with a yellow hexagon, 6 green triangles, and 2 blues rhombuses.

Teacher: Can you show me where the thirds are?

Mary: Here's a yellow and six triangles is a part.

Teacher: And I see two blues. But I don't think your design is one third yellow. It is almost one third yellow. Can you figure out what to do to make it one third yellow? Can you show me the three equal parts?

Mary stares at her paper for a bit.

Teacher: You said it was one third yellow. So is yellow one of your equal parts?

She points to the yellow hexagon.

Teacher: What is another third of your design?

She points to some of the green triangles on her paper. Since I can't really tell what she is thinking, I wonder if rebuilding the design with blocks will help.

Teacher: Let's build it again. You used six greens, right?

I help her get the pieces she needs. She begins arranging the pieces.

Teacher: And two blue ones.

Mary: Yeah. . . . Wait, . . . Wait. Hold on.

I watch as she carefully replicates what she'd colored on the paper.

Teacher: Can you show me the three equal parts? Where are the thirds in your design?

I suggest that she put all the pieces together into hexagons. She puts all the greens together.

Mary: I need one more of these blue ones.

Teacher: Why do you need one more blue?

Mary: Because I have to make three wholes, and I only have two blues. And three blues make a whole.

She was busily rearranging the pieces into her original design.

Mary: Where will I put it?

I could see that the inclusion of this additional blue piece was going to ruin the symmetry of her design. I wondered if this helped cause the problem in the first place.

Teacher: Well, do you have to use a *blue* piece?

Mary: I could use two greens! They equal one blue.

And she happily found a place for them that kept the symmetry of her design.

Tamara

Tamara is a good math thinker. She has great number sense and sees herself as a good math student. She, too, had been excited about the challenge of creating a design that was one third yellow. However, she came to me with a forlorn look, "I can't do a third yellow." First of all, she was trying to use several yellow parts in addition to several parts made of the other colors.

Teacher: What does thirds mean?

Tamara: Three parts.

Teacher: What needs to be true about those three parts?

Tamara: They have to be the same, equal.

I asked her to make a design that was all yellow, where she could see thirds. She put down three yellow hexagons.

Teacher: Why does this design have thirds? Why are these thirds?

Tamara: Because there are three parts and they're equal.

Teacher: Where are the three equal parts?

She points to each, one at a time.

Teacher: Where is one third? If you wanted to make a design that was only one *third* yellow, what would you have to do?

Tamara: Use other colors.

Teacher: Can you show me what you mean?

Another student needed me. When I came back, Tamara had a design made up of two yellows and six blues.

Teacher: Can you show me where your thirds are?

Tamara pointed to the two yellow parts and then began counting up the blues and putting them into hexagons.

Tamara: It isn't thirds. . . . It's fourths.

Teacher: Do you have to add to it or take something away?

I knew she really could have done either, but I wanted her to think about a design equal to three hexagons before she tried anything more complicated.

Tamara: I have to take a whole away.

Teacher: You have to take a whole away or do you need to take a hexagon away?

Tamara (smiling): A hexagon.

Teacher: So what are you taking away, something yellow or something blue?

Tamara: Something yellow.

She happily slides the yellow away and begins to copy her design onto the paper. But I was to see in other designs that she was still struggling with these expanded ideas about fractions and equivalency.

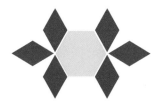

It takes a while for the students to grapple with these ideas. I plan on spending a good amount of time on this important activity. All halves aren't red trapezoids! All thirds aren't blue rhombuses!

Mary and Tamara are both working with a central idea in understanding fractions—that the fractional part is related to a particular whole. In work with fractions, students often start with a whole and divide it into fractional parts. These students are used to thinking of one of the pattern blocks as a whole and using it to show fractions. However, building up *from* a part ($\frac{1}{3}$) *to* a whole provides a new challenge. In addition, the whole is now not just one pattern block but a design made up of a number of blocks. The teacher helps the students visualize the relationships of fractional part and whole by consistently referring to the pattern block

representation: "Can you show me where the thirds are?" By manipulating the representation, they can see if they do have three equal parts, one of which is yellow, and, with the teacher's support, revise their representation.

Questions for Discussion

1. **What do students need to understand about fractions to make designs that are "half yellow" or "one third yellow?"**

2. **What do Mary and Tamara understand about thirds? What confuses them? What steps does Ms. Thompson take to help them work through their confusion?**

3. **What experiences have your students had with these activities? How have you helped them make the necessary shifts in their thinking about fractions?**

Language and Representation

Count and Compare: A Visual Representation for Multiplication

In this case, Katrina Sajak reflects on an extension she made to the game Count and Compare *to maximize the use of arrays as a visual representation for multiplication and to address the diverse needs of the students in her classroom.*

Recently, a third-grade colleague and I were discussing some concerns about the array game *Count and Compare.* When her students played the game at home, some parents had reported that their children were "bored" because they already "knew their multiplication facts." However, this game helps students develop and understand a visual representation for multiplication and is about much more than merely practicing multiplication facts. I wondered if we were taking full advantage of the opportunities for the learning this game offers.

I shared a modification I made to *Count and Compare* to add an element of challenge for the range of learners in my classroom. Students who were using the game to help them learn and practice the factor pairs were supported by the spatial comparisons offered by the basic game. However, I wanted to ensure that all students were using the game to deepen their understanding of multiplication. I decided to ask each pair of students to come to the discussion with an "interesting comparison" they had worked with. I particularly pushed those students who I knew were already fluent with the factor pairs represented by the arrays by asking them to describe the relationship between the arrays they were comparing. (For this work, I paired together students who had a similar level of familiarity with factor pairs.)

As students played, I observed and took notes on what they said. The result was an amazing explosion of ideas that I wanted to be sure we considered as a group. Therefore, as students shared their "interesting comparisons" in the discussion at the end of the session, we grouped them into categories on a piece of chart paper. The categories were as follows:

Arrays we found with equivalent area

Example: a 3×8 equals a 2×12

Arrays for which the area of one is half or double the area of the other

Example: two 3×6s make a 6×6

Arrays for which the area of one is one-fourth or four times the area of the other

Example: four 3×3s make a 6×6 or a 3×3 is one fourth of a 6×6

Arrays we found that were "close calls"

Example: a 7×7 and a 12×4 have almost the same area

Arrays for which one big array is equal to two or more smaller arrays

Example: a 10×5 equals a 3×5 plus a 3×5 plus a 4×5

These comparisons provided ways to clarify some things about the meaning and characteristics of multiplication and how it differs from other operations. For example, when comparing a 6×6 array with a 5×7 array, some students initially thought they must have equal area because one dimension "went up by one and the other went down by one." As they talked about this relationship that had worked for addition ($6 + 6 = 5 + 7$), they realized that the same didn't hold true for multiplication ($6 \times 6 \neq 5 \times 7$).

We were out of time for the day, but I wanted the ideas on the "interesting comparisons" chart to be accessible to as many students as possible. I asked a few students to be prepared at the start of the next math class to use array cards to represent some of the relationships they had found as they played *Count and Compare.* This was the result.

Tom and Lisa had contributed $6 \times 4 = 3 \times 8$ to our list of equivalent arrays. They placed the 6×4 array on top of the 3×8 array and observed that the "sticking out" part of the 6×4 was an extra 6×1, and the "sticking out" piece of the 3×8 was an extra 2×3. They could see the equivalence because $2 \times 3 = 1 \times 6$, since both equal six squares.

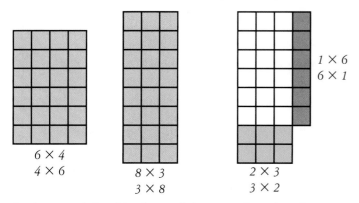

6 × 4
4 × 6

8 × 3
3 × 8

1 × 6
6 × 1

2 × 3
3 × 2

Rashawn and Cynthia observed that $7 \times 6 = (4 \times 6) + (2 \times 6) + (1 \times 6)$. They represented this relationship for the class by building the $(4 \times 6) + (2 \times 6) + (1 \times 6)$ with three array cards right on top of the 7×6 array card. This pair tried the same approach with another pair of arrays and came up with this equation: $(7 \times 3) + (7 \times 4) = 7 \times 7$.

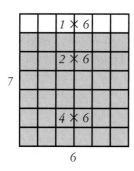

1 × 6
2 × 6
7
4 × 6
6

Jill and Nora observed that "four 2×2s make a 4×4." They demonstrated to the class how four 2×2 arrays would be required to cover a 4×4 array. They also reported that "a 2×2 is a third of a 2×6" and demonstrated how three 2×2 arrays would cover a 2×6 array.

My students also began to think of *generalizations about comparing arrays* that you can make by comparing their dimensions. They put it this way:

- "If both dimensions of one array are bigger than both dimensions of the other array, then the array with the bigger dimensions is larger." This was demonstrated by placing the array with the bigger dimensions over the smaller one and showing that "no parts were sticking out."

- "If one dimension of an array is the same as one dimension of another array, then whichever array has the largest other dimension is the bigger one." For example, when comparing a 3×8 and a 4×8, students reasoned: "$8 = 8$. Since $4 > 3$, then $4 \times 8 > 3 \times 8$."

- "When you are comparing two arrays that are the same size (area), the one that has the biggest dimension will also have the smallest dimension. The other array will be closer to a square."

As I looked back, I was satisfied that we had taken full advantage of the mathematical opportunities inspired by *Count and Compare*. Students who needed practice with multiplication facts were provided with a new way of visualizing the factor pairs and their products. In addition, they and all students were able to use this activity to explore the relationships between different factor pairs as well as the properties of the operation of multiplication.

This case demonstrates Ms. Sajak's awareness of two things: the differing needs of the students in her classroom and the richness of the mathematical ideas that can be explored through the game Count and Compare. *By asking students to pay greater attention to the comparisons, to be explicit about what they were noticing, and to represent the relationships they found, she was able to address those diverse needs while maximizing the opportunity for all students to explore the mathematical ideas. The challenge remains, for her and her colleague, to effectively communicate this use of the game to the parents of their students.*

Questions for Discussion

1. Ms. Sajak asked her students to find an interesting comparison as they played the game *Count and Compare.* What important mathematical ideas emerged as the students shared, discussed, and represented the comparisons they found? Which ideas might be particularly fruitful to pursue further?

2. How could Ms. Sajak and her colleague highlight the important ideas in *Count and Compare* for parents? How can you communicate to parents the opportunities for learning provided by a game or activity and support such use at home?

Using Representations in Brownie Problems: What Do You Call a Third of a Half?

After working on an activity in which a given number of paper "brownies" are shared among a given number of people, for example, five brownies shared among three people, Ms. King looks over the students' work to determine what her next steps should be. She is particularly concerned with helping her students represent each situation and accurately name and record the fractional parts.

I saw that several students had shared the brownies correctly but didn't know how to accurately record the amounts. It was difficult for them to move between representing the situation and recording the quantity. A few did not have correct shares; some did not even have the required number of brownies in their work. I know that some students need to cut all the brownies up rather than sharing whole brownies first. Other students don't see that cutting up all the brownies is a possible strategy for solving the problems. Some students think that unless there is the same number of brownies as people, then it is not possible to share the brownies fairly.

My conversation with Yukio shows some typical difficulties. Even though earlier in the unit Yukio had successfully cut up one brownie to share with two, three, or more people and had also made the *Fraction Sets,* he was not able to make sense of the current situation. When I joined him, he was working on

the problem "five brownies shared among three people." He knew people were cutting up the brownies, but he wasn't seeing any connection between the number of people and the size of the pieces. He randomly cut pieces and glued them on the paper. He wasn't able to explain where the individual shares were on his paper nor was he able to explain if he had the total number of brownies in the original problem. He wasn't able to recombine the pieces to see if there really were five brownies. He had no sense of the sizes of the pieces. Like some other students, he started cutting; when he was done, he had no idea how big the pieces were or whether his solution worked.

At first he wanted to cut the brownies up in fourths. Since he had already tried unsuccessfully to solve the problem that way, I decided to redirect him. I thought that it would be useful for him to think about sharing whole brownies first. He would have fewer small pieces to keep track of, and it would be easier for him to be able to count up and find the five original brownies in his solution.

Teacher: So you have five brownies. What can you do to share them with three people?

He began to fold them in fourths.

Teacher: Do you need to cut them up to share them with three people?

Yukio: You need more brownies.

I think he meant that he needed more brownies because there weren't enough *whole* brownies to share equally for everyone.

Teacher: You have five brownies and three people. Can you give anybody some brownie right now?

Yukio: Yes, I could give them each a whole.

Teacher: Yes. Why don't you do that?

Yukio gave one brownie to each imaginary person.

Yukio: But now we have two brownies left.

Teacher: Okay, is there something we could do with the two brownies that would share them fairly?

Yukio: Cut them in half?

I had hoped he would say thirds, but it is hard for kids to think about thirds. It seems easy for them to share with two or four people, but when faced with three people, they still want to cut into fourths. While there's something easy about halving halves, the idea of thirds and sixths is trickier.

Teacher: Okay, why don't you try that?

Yukio folded one of the remaining brownies, cut it in half and gave each half to two of the people.

Then he picked up one of the whole brownies he'd already given out and was going to cut it in half.

Teacher: Let's leave these wholes here, Yukio.

I wanted him to leave those three whole brownies that he already distributed alone. I knew I was leading him, but I hoped this would help him develop some understanding about the relationships between how many people and how many brownies in these problems.

He picked up the remaining whole brownie, folded it, and cut it.

Teacher: What do you need to do to make it fair?

He gave one half to the third person.

Teacher: Cool! Is it fair now?

Yukio: Yes.

Teacher: How many brownies does each person have so far?

Yukio: One and a half.

Yukio looked at the half of a brownie he still had in his hand.

Teacher: But you still have a piece of brownie left? Don't cut it yet. (He starts to fold the half in half.) What do you need to do to that piece so that everyone has the same amount?

Yukio: Cut it into three pieces . . . into small thirds.

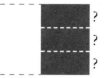

I was impressed that he was referring to the new pieces as thirds. A few minutes ago thirds did not appear to be a part of this thinking.

Teacher: A small third. Cool! You're right, but it's not a third.

Yukio: It's a fourth!

Teacher: It's not a fourth. But it has a name.

Yukio: Eighth!

Teacher: It's not an eighth either. Don't cut it yet.

I was afraid we'd never figure out what the piece was called if it was cut up.

Teacher: What makes it feel like it's a small third?

Yukio: Because there are three of these.

He has folded the half in thirds.

Teacher: Yes, there are three pieces. Don't cut it yet.

Yukio: So they're thirds, but they're small.

Teacher: Yes, they are small, and there are three of them. But are they a third of a brownie? What is it a third of?

Yukio: It's a third of a half.

Teacher: Yes, it's a third of a half. Don't cut it yet. Before we cut it up, we have to figure out how big these pieces are. You are right! They are a third of a half. But what is their name?

I reached for a whole brownie.

Teacher: Here's a whole brownie. (I folded it in half and then into thirds, just as Yukio had. I put it down next to the half he had folded into "small thirds.")

Yukio: It's a sixth!

Teacher: Why?

Yukio: Because there are three on this side and three on this side.

Teacher: Excellent! So when you cut up that half of your brownie, the pieces aren't going to be thirds, they're going to be sixths because they are a third of a half.

I thought it was important to restate Yukio's thinking. I hope it helps!

Teacher: I liked how you called them "small thirds," but they aren't thirds.

Yukio: They are sixths. There are six of them.

He points to the whole brownies we had folded.

I asked Yukio to glue the shares for each person on his paper and to write the number of brownies that each person got. When I returned later, I was pleased with the result.

$$1 + \tfrac{1}{2} + \tfrac{1}{6} \qquad 1 + \tfrac{1}{2} + \tfrac{1}{6} \qquad 1 + \tfrac{1}{2} + \tfrac{1}{6}$$

While many of Ms. King's students are comfortable dividing one brownie into fractional parts, representing and recording the fractions involved with dividing five brownies among three people proves to be more challenging. Because students are more experienced working with halves and fourths, dividing brownies among three people adds another layer of complexity for the students to represent. In this case, we see how Ms. King worked with one of her students to help him work through his confusion and correctly represent and identify each person's fair share.

Questions for Discussion

1. When Ms. King observes him, how is Yukio attempting to solve this problem of dividing five brownies between three people? What are the first steps Ms. King takes to help him solve and represent this problem?

2. What issues arise for Yukio as he tries to decide how to divide the remaining half brownie? What steps does Ms. King take to help Yukio work through the confusion he is having about what to call a third of a half?

3. Have you encountered similar confusion about sharing many brownies among the students in your classroom? What next steps would you put in place for Yukio or for students like him?

PART 8

Scope and Sequence

LOOKING BACK AT:

Grade 2

Number and Operations	104
Patterns and Functions	109
Data Analysis	109
Geometry	110
Measurement	111
Classroom Routines	112

Grade 3

Number and Operations	114
Patterns, Functions, and Change	117
Data and Probability	118
Geometry	119
Measurement	120
Classroom Routines	121
Ten-Minute Math	121

LOOKING FORWARD TO:

Grade 4

Number and Operations	122
Patterns, Functions, and Change	125
Data and Probability	126
Geometry	127
Measurement	127
Ten-Minute Math	128

The strands are divided into Math Emphases.

The Math Emphases may be covered in one or more units. The Math Emphases are further subdivided into Math Focus Points.

Each strand is labeled with a grade level.

The content is organized around five strands.

GRADE 3

Number and Operations

The Base-Ten Number System Understanding the equivalence of one group and the discrete units that comprise it

Unit 1 Math Focus Points

- Recognizing and representing the place value of each digit in 2- and 3-digit numbers
- Using equivalencies among pennies, dimes, and dollars
- Finding different combinations of 100s, 10s, and 1s for a number and recognizing their equivalence (e.g., 1 hundred, 3 tens, and 7 ones equals 1 hundred, 2 tens, and 17 ones, or 13 tens and 7 ones)
- Recognizing and demonstrating the equivalence of one 100 to ten 10s and one 10 to ten 1s
- Recognizing and using coin equivalencies

Unit 3 Math Focus Points

- Constructing 1,000 from groups of 100
- Recognizing and representing the number of tens in 3-digit numbers
- Representing the structure of 3-digit numbers as being composed of 100s, 10s, and 1s
- Using the value of each place to make 2- and 3-digit numbers closest to 100

GRADE 2

Number and Operations

Counting and Quantity Developing strategies for accurately counting a set of objects by ones and groups

Unit 1 Math Focus Points

- ◆ Counting sets of up to 60 objects
- ◆ Developing strategies for counting accurately
- ◆ Counting a quantity in more than one way
- ◆ Developing and analyzing visual images for quantities up to 10
- ◆ Counting by groups of 10

Unit 3 Math Focus Points

- ◆ Looking at patterns and developing fluency with skip counting by 2s, 5s, and 10s
- ◆ Considering the relationship between skip counting and grouping
- ◆ Counting by groups of 2, 5, and 10
- ◆ Noticing and describing a 2:1 relationship (e.g., there are 2 legs for every 1 person)
- ◆ Solving problems that involve equal groups
- ◆ Knowing that the size of a group remains constant no matter how it is counted (by 1s, 2s, 5s, or 10s)

Counting and Quantity Counting by equal groups

Unit 3 Math Focus Points

- ◆ Investigating numbers that can and cannot be made into groups of two or two equal groups
- ◆ Understanding that any number that can be divided into groups of two can also be divided into two equal groups (and vice versa)
- ◆ Characterizing even and odd numbers as those that do or do not make groups of two (partners) and two equal groups (teams)
- ◆ Considering whether observations about even or odd numbers apply to all even numbers or all odd numbers

Unit 5 Math Focus Points

- ◆ Counting by and adding equal groups, such as 2s and 5s

Unit 6 Math Focus Points

- ◆ Skip counting by 2s, 5s, and 10s
- ◆ Identifying patterns in the multiples of 2, 5, and 10
- ◆ Using the relationship between 5 and 10, and between nickels and dimes, to solve problems
- ◆ Thinking about the structure of 100 in terms of groups of 5 and 10

Unit 8 Math Focus Points

- ◆ Counting a set of objects by equal groups

Counting and Quantity Developing an understanding of the magnitude and sequence of numbers up to 100

Unit 1 Math Focus Points

- ◆ Using the number line to reason about, and keep track of information about, the magnitude and relationship of numbers
- ◆ Developing an understanding of the structure of the 100 chart
- ◆ Counting, writing, and reading numbers sequentially from 1 to 100 and beyond
- ◆ Identifying and using patterns in the structure of the number system

Unit 6 Math Focus Points

- ◆ Becoming familiar with the structure of the 100 chart
- ◆ Developing fluency with the sequence of numbers from 1 to 100
- ◆ Finding and using patterns in the sequence of numbers
- ◆ Using the 100 chart to reason about, and keep track of, information about the magnitude and relationship of numbers

Whole Number Operations **Making sense of and developing strategies to solve addition and subtraction problems with totals up to 45**

Unit 1 Math Focus Points

- Generating equivalent expressions for a number
- Comparing two amounts under 45 to find the difference
- Combining two quantities, with totals up to 45
- Visualizing, retelling, and modeling the action of addition and subtraction (as removal) situations
- Using known combinations (e.g., combinations that make 10) to compose, decompose, and combine numbers
- Subtracting a quantity from a whole of up to 30
- Solving addition and subtraction (as removal) story problems
- Doubling a quantity

Unit 3 Math Focus Points

- Using known combinations to add two or more numbers
- Comparing a number to 20 to find the difference
- Visualizing, retelling, and modelling the action of a variety of addition and subtraction situations
- Developing strategies for solving a variety of addition and subtraction story problems with totals up to 45 and recording work
- Solving problems with an unknown change
- Combining coins to a total of 50¢
- Solving an addition story problem by counting on or breaking numbers apart

Unit 4 Math Focus Points

- Developing strategies for combining multiple addends

Whole Number Operations **Making sense of and developing strategies to solve addition and subtraction problems with totals up to 100**

Unit 6 Math Focus Points

- Developing efficient methods for adding and subtracting 2-digit numbers
- Adding tens and ones to combine 2-digit numbers
- Adding 2-digit numbers by keeping one number whole
- Noticing what happens to the tens place when a multiple of 10 is added or subtracted
- Naming and comparing strategies for adding and subtracting two-digit numbers
- Determining the difference between a number and a multiple of 10 up to 100.
- Adding 2-digit numbers
- Adding multiples of 5 and 10, up to 100
- Adding coin amounts, up to $1.00
- Determining the difference between a given amount and $1.00
- Adding and subtracting 10 and multiples of 10 to/from any number
- Subtracting amounts from 100 or $1.00, down to 0

Unit 8 Math Focus Points

- Subtracting amounts from 100
- Visualizing, retelling, and modeling the action of addition and subtraction situations
- Developing efficient methods for adding, subtracting, and notating strategies
- Solving subtraction problems by subtracting in parts
- Solving subtraction problems by adding up or subtracting back to find the difference
- Comparing problems in which the amount subtracted differs by 1
- Adding 2-digit numbers by keeping one number whole

◈ Adding 2-digit numbers by adding tens and ones

◈ Noticing what happens to place value when two 2-digit numbers with a sum over 100 are combined

◈ Thinking about what happens if you subtract 1 more or 1 less

Unit 9 Math Focus Point

◈ Solving comparison problems by finding the difference between two measurements

Whole Number Operations Using manipulatives, drawings, tools, and notation to show strategies and solutions

Unit 1 Math Focus Points

◈ Establishing use of tools, routines, and expectations for math class

◈ Using standard notation ($>$, $<$, $+$, $-$, $=$) to describe arrangements of cubes, to record expressions that equal a given number, to compare quantities, to represent addition and subtraction situations, and to represent doubling

◈ Using the number line to reason about, and keep track of information about, the magnitude and relationship of numbers

◈ Recording strategies for solving problems, including addition and subtraction story problems

◈ Using equations to record

◈ Connecting standard notation for addition and subtraction ($+$, $-$, $=$) to the quantities and actions that the signs and symbols represent

◈ Using a rectangular array to model doubling

Unit 3 Math Focus Points

◈ Using the calculator as a mathematical tool

◈ Using standard notation ($+$, $-$, $=$) to represent a variety of addition and subtraction situations

◈ Telling stories to match given equations

◈ Using tally marks to represent groups of 5

Unit 6 Math Focus Points

◈ Writing an equation that represents a problem

◈ Developing efficient methods for notating addition and subtraction strategies

◈ Visualizing and making jumps of multiples of 5 on the 100 chart

◈ Using the 100 chart and the number line to model addition

◈ Using coins to model adding 5s and 10s

Unit 8 Math Focus Points

◈ Using cubes and the number line to show how addition combinations are related

◈ Representing the action of subtraction and addition situations using notation ($-$, $+$, $=$)

Whole Number Operations Understanding the properties of addition and subtraction

Unit 3 Math Focus Points

◈ Considering whether reordering three addends results in the same total

◈ Considering a generalization about reordering addends for all numbers

◈ Considering whether reordering the numbers in a subtraction problem results in the same total

◈ Considering the relationship between addition and subtraction

Whole Number Operations **Adding even and odd numbers**

Unit 8 Math Focus Points

- Characterizing even and odd numbers as those that do or do not make groups of two (partners) and two equal groups (teams)
- Investigating what happens with partners and teams when two groups are combined
- Finding combinations of odd and even numbers that make given numbers or determining that these combinations are not possible
- Making and testing conjectures about adding even and odd numbers
- Making and justifying generalizations about adding even and odd numbers

Computational Fluency **Knowing addition combinations to 10 + 10**

Unit 1 Math Focus Points

- Developing and achieving fluency with the make 10, +1, and +2 addition combinations
- Finding two addends that make 10
- Finding the missing addend to make a total of 10
- Doubling a quantity
- Developing fluency with the doubles combinations

Unit 2 Math Focus Points

- Reviewing known addition combinations (combinations of 10, +1, +2)
- Developing fluency with the doubles combinations to 10 + 10
- Achieving fluency with the doubles combinations

Unit 3 Math Focus Points

- Relating the doubles and near-doubles combinations
- Developing fluency with the near-doubles combinations
- Adding 10 to any number (or any number to 10)
- Developing fluency with the +10 combinations
- Achieving fluency with the near-doubles combinations

Unit 4 Math Focus Point

- Achieving fluency with the +10 combinations

Unit 8 Math Focus Points

- Relating unknown combinations to known combinations
- Developing and achieving fluency with the +9 and remaining combinations

The Base-Ten Number System **Understanding the equivalence of one group and the discrete units that comprise it**

Unit 1 Math Focus Points

- Identifying coins and their values
- Identifying how many pennies each coin is worth
- Identifying and using coin equivalencies

Unit 3 Math Focus Points

- Identifying coins and their values
- Identifying and using coin equivalencies
- Recognizing that the first digit of a 2-digit number designates the number of groups of 10 and the second digit designates the number of ones
- Solving problems about 10s and 1s

- Using a place-value model to represent a number as 10s and 1s
- Finding as many combinations of a number as possible, using only 10s and 1s
- Recognizing that different combinations of 10s and 1s for the same number are equivalent (e.g., 4 tens and 6 ones = 3 tens and 16 ones, etc.)

Unit 6 Math Focus Points

- Organizing cubes into 10s and 1s
- Using a place-value model to represent a number as 10s and 1s
- Using coin equivalencies
- Working with the relationship between 1, 10, and 100

Rational Numbers Understanding fractions as equal parts of a whole

Unit 7 Math Focus Points

- Finding equal parts of a whole and naming them with fractions, (e.g., $\frac{1}{2}$ is one of two equal parts; $\frac{1}{3}$ is one of three equal parts, and so on)
- Naming fractional parts that have numerators greater than 1 (e.g., $\frac{2}{3}, \frac{2}{4}, \frac{3}{4}$)
- Showing one half of an object
- Determining whether a block is half of another block
- Determining whether a region is half of a given rectangle
- Seeing different ways to make fourths of a square
- Recognizing the equivalence of different fourths of the same object
- Identifying halves, thirds, and fourths of regions
- Identifying $\frac{2}{3}, \frac{2}{4}$, and $\frac{3}{4}$ of regions

Rational Numbers Understanding fractions as equal parts of a group

Unit 7 Math Focus Points

- Finding equal parts of a group and naming them with fractions (e.g., $\frac{1}{2}$ is one of two equal parts; $\frac{1}{3}$ is one of three equal parts, and so on)
- Finding one half of a set
- Finding thirds and fourths of sets
- Finding fractions of sets
- Solving problems about finding halves of quantities in different contexts
- Solving problems that result in mixed numbers

Rational Numbers Using terms and notation

Unit 7 Math Focus Points

- Learning the term *one half* and the notation $\frac{1}{2}$
- Learning the term *one fourth* and the notation $\frac{1}{4}$
- Learning the term *one third* and the notation $\frac{1}{3}$
- Learning the terms and notation for fractions that contain more than one part (e.g., $\frac{2}{3}, \frac{2}{4}$, and $\frac{3}{4}$)
- Learning the terms and notation for mixed numbers (e.g., one and a half and $1\frac{1}{2}$)

GRADE 2

Patterns and Functions

Linear Relationships Describing and representing ratios

Unit 5 Math Focus Points

- Describing the relationship between two quantities in a constant ratio situation
- Using tables to represent the ratio relationship between two quantities
- Finding the value of one quantity in a constant ratio situation, given the value of the other

Using Tables and Graphs Using tables to represent change

Unit 5 Math Focus Points

- Connecting numbers in a table to the situation they represent
- Using conventional language for a table and its parts: rows, columns
- Describing the pattern in the numbers in a column and interpreting the pattern in terms of the situation the table represents
- Describing what is the same about situations that look different but can be represented by the same table
- Describing how the two numbers in the row of a table are connected to the situation the table represents
- Using information in a table to determine the relationship between two quantities

Number Sequences Constructing, describing, and extending number sequences with constant increments generated by various contexts

Unit 5 Math Focus Points

- Extending a repeating pattern
- Identifying the unit of a repeating pattern
- Creating a repeating pattern that has the same structure as, but different elements than, another repeating pattern (e.g., a red-blue pattern and a clap-tap head pattern)
- Defining even and odd numbers
- Determining and describing the number sequence associated with one of the elements in an AB, ABC, ABCD, or AABBC patterns (e.g., 2, 4, 6, 8, . . .; 3, 6, 9, . . .; 1, 4, 7, . . .)
- Determining the element of a repeating pattern associated with a particular counting number in AB, ABC, ABCD, or AABBC patterns (e.g., what color is the 8th element in a red-blue repeating pattern?)
- Determining how and why the same number sequence can be generated by different contexts

GRADE 2

Data Analysis

Data Analysis Sorting and classifying data

Unit 4 Math Focus Points

- Grouping data into categories based on similar attributes
- Sorting a set of data by two attributes at one time
- Sorting the same set of data in different ways

Data Analysis **Representing data**

Unit 4 Math Focus Points

- Representing a set of data sorted into categories
- Using a Venn diagram to represent a sorted set of data
- Using equations to show how the sum of the responses in each category equals the total responses collected
- Comparing ways of organizing data
- Comparing representations of a set of data
- Ordering, representing, and describing a set of numerical data
- Representing data on a line plot

Data Analysis **Describing data**

Unit 1 Math Focus Points

- Making predictions about data

Unit 4 Math Focus Points

- Describing what the data show about the group surveyed
- Interpreting a data representation including a line plot
- Describing important features of a data set
- Describing a set of numerical data
- Comparing two sets of data
- Developing a hypothesis based on a set of data

Data Analysis **Designing and carrying out a data investigation**

Unit 1 Math Focus Points

- Collecting, counting, representing, discussing, interpreting, and comparing data

Unit 4 Math Focus Points

- Choosing a survey question
- Making a plan for collecting data
- Making predictions about data to be collected
- Collecting and recording data from a survey
- Interpreting and sharing results from a data investigation

GRADE 2

Geometry

Features of Shape **Composing and decomposing two-dimensional and three-dimensional shapes**

Unit 1 Math Focus Points

- Fitting shapes together to cover an area

Unit 2 Math Focus Points

- Combining shapes to make a new shape
- Covering a region, without gaps or overlaps, with a single shape or multiple shapes
- Covering a region, without gaps or overlaps, using different shapes
- Combining 3-D shapes to make a 3-D whole
- Drawing 3-D shapes

Features of Shape Describing, identifying, comparing, and sorting 2-dimensional and 3-dimensional shapes

Unit 2 Math Focus Points

- Describing attributes and sorting 2-dimensional shapes
- Identifying names and attributes of 2-dimensional and 3-dimensional shapes
- Attending to features of 3-dimensional shapes, particularly the number and shape of faces
- Identifying categories for 2-dimensional shapes
- Identifying a 3-dimensional shape by touch
- Sorting polygons by the number of sides
- Sorting quadrilaterals by angle
- Identifying quadrilaterals as shapes with 4 sides
- Identifying rectangles as 4-sided shapes with 4 right angles
- Identifying important features of a rectangle
- Defining *biggest* in different ways
- Ordering rectangles from biggest to smallest
- Recognizing that rectangular prisms have rectangular faces
- Recognizing which faces of a rectangular prism are the same size and shape
- Constructing a rectangular prism from rectangles
- Visualizing and describing rectangular prisms
- Comparing rectangular prisms

Features of Shape Exploring mirror symmetry

Unit 2 Math Focus Points

- Describing and identifying objects and designs that have mirror symmetry
- Constructing 2-dimensional and 3-dimensional symmetrical designs with mirror symmetry
- Reflecting a shape across a line of symmetry

- Exploring symmetry by folding and cutting paper patterns
- Identifying lines of symmetry
- Orienting shapes so that a line of symmetry aligns with a mirror (*Shapes* Software)
- Determine what makes a design symmetrical

GRADE 2

Measurement

Area Measurement Visualizing the structure of arrays

Unit 2 Math Focus Points

- Defining *biggest* in different ways
- Ordering rectangles from biggest to smallest
- Covering rectangles with arrays of tiles
- Arranging square tiles in rectangular arrays
- Constructing and describing rectangular arrays of tiles
- Making different rectangular arrays using the same number of tiles
- Drawing rectangles by attending to the lengths of the sides

Linear Measurement Understanding length

Unit 9 Math Focus Points

- Comparing two lengths
- Using direct and indirect comparison to identify equal lengths
- Identifying length and width as different dimensions of an object

Linear Measurement **Using linear units**

Unit 9 Math Focus Points

◆ Iterating units to measure length
◆ Estimating and calculating length using units that are related by a 2:1 ratio
◆ Identifying strategies for accurate measurement
◆ Considering sources of measurement error
◆ Understanding that different-sized units yield different counts (the smaller the unit, the higher the count)
◆ Establishing the need for and using a common unit in order to compare measurements
◆ Identifying and labeling partial units
◆ Recognizing that, given equal counts of two different units, the larger unit marks off a longer length

Linear Measurement **Measuring with standard units**

Unit 9 Math Focus Points

◆ Establishing the need for and using a standard unit of measure
◆ Creating and using a 12-inch measuring tool
◆ Iterating a 12-inch measuring tool
◆ Measuring lengths that are longer than 12 inches
◆ Using a ruler as a standard measuring tool
◆ Comparing a variety of measurement tools
◆ Becoming familiar with the terms *inches, feet, yards; centimeters* and *meters* as standard units of measure
◆ Using inches, feet, yards, centimeters, and meters to describe lengths
◆ Comparing centimeters and inches

Time **Representing time and calculating duration**

Unit 9 Math Focus Points

◆ Representing time as a horizontal sequence
◆ Connecting a time, its digital notation, and its representation on an analog clock to a timeline
◆ Naming and using notation for times that are 30 and 15 minutes before or after the hour
◆ Associating times with daily events
◆ Using a timeline to determine duration
◆ Moving forward and backward along a timeline in multiples of hours, half hours, and quarter hours
◆ Using a timeline to show a 24-hour period
◆ Recording events on a timeline

GRADE 2

Classroom Routines

How Many Pockets?

Units 1–9 Math Focus Points

◆ Making predictions about data
◆ Collecting, counting, representing, discussing, interpreting, and comparing data
◆ Counting by groups
◆ Counting a quantity in more than one way
◆ Using known combinations (i.e. combinations that make 10) to combine numbers
◆ Developing strategies for solving addition problems with many addends
◆ Using a place value model to represent a number as 10's and 1's

- Recognizing that the first digit of a 2-digit number designates the number of groups of 10 and the second digit designates the number of ones
- Identifying coins and their values
- Identifying and using coin equivalencies

Today's Number

Units 1–9 Math Focus Points

- Generating equivalent expressions for a number
- Developing fluency with addition and subtraction
- Using standard notation $(+, -, =)$ to record expressions and write equations
- Using the number line and 100 chart to reason about the magnitude and relationship of numbers
- Skip counting by 2's, 5's, and 10's
- Identifying patterns in the multiples of 2, 5, and 10

Quick Images

Units 1–9 Math Focus Points

- Developing and analyzing visual images for quantities up to 10
- Developing fluency with the addition combinations to $10 + 10$
- Using known combinations (i.e. combinations that make 10) to combine numbers
- Recreating images of dots arranged in two by five arrays
- Using standard notation $(+, -, =)$ to write equations
- Identifying names and attributes of 2-D shapes
- Using arrays and standard notation $(+, =)$ to represent doubles to $10 + 10$
- Combining groups of tens and ones
- Adding or subtracting 10 to/from a two-digit number

- Noticing what happens to the tens place when a multiple of 10 is added or subtracted to/from a two-digit number
- Identifying coins and their values
- Adding coin amounts
- Using ratio relationships to solve problems
- Solving problems about an unknown change

What Time Is It?

Units 1–9 Math Focus Points

- Using clocks as tools for keeping track of and measuring time
- Naming, notating, and telling time to the hour, half hour, and quarter hour on digital and analog clocks
- Associating times on the hour and half hour with daily events
- Determining what time it will be when given start and elapsed times that are multiples of 15 minutes
- Determining the number of minutes in hours, half hours, and quarter hours
- Counting by 5's
- Seeing a timeline as a representation of events over time
- Using a timeline to keep track of and compare time and events
- Determining the length of a given interval (e.g., 8:30 to 9:30) or activity (e.g., math class)
- Solving problems involving elapsed time

Number and Operations

The Base-Ten Number System **Understanding the equivalence of one group and the discrete units that comprise it**

Unit 1 Math Focus Points
- Recognizing and representing the place value of each digit in 2- and 3-digit numbers
- Using equivalencies among pennies, dimes, and dollars
- Finding different combinations of 100s, 10s, and 1s for a number and recognizing their equivalence (e.g., 1 hundred, 3 tens, and 7 ones equals 1 hundred, 2 tens, and 17 ones, or 13 tens and 7 ones)
- Recognizing and demonstrating the equivalence of one 100 to ten 10s and one 10 to ten 1s
- Recognizing and using coin equivalencies

Unit 3 Math Focus Points
- Constructing 1,000 from groups of 100
- Recognizing and representing the number of tens in 3-digit numbers
- Representing the structure of 3-digit numbers as being composed of 100s, 10s, and 1s
- Using the value of each place to make 2- and 3-digit numbers closest to 100

The Base-Ten Number System **Extending knowledge of the number system to 1,000**

Unit 3 Math Focus Points
- Reading, writing, and sequencing numbers to 1,000
- Using place value to determine the size of any number to 1,000

Unit 8 Math Focus Points
- Reading and writing numbers in the thousands

Computational Fluency **Adding and subtracting accurately and efficiently**

Unit 1 Math Focus Points
- Adding and subtracting multiples of 10
- Solving addition problems with 2-digit numbers by using strategies that involve breaking numbers apart by place or adding one number in parts
- Solving addition problems with 2-digit numbers that involve more than 10 ones in the ones place and explaining the effect on the sum
- Finding the difference between a 2-digit number and 100
- Adding pennies and dimes to sums up to $2.00
- Learning/reviewing addition combinations up to 10 + 10
- Using knowledge of place value to find pairs of 2-digit numbers that add to 100 or a number close to 100
- Using known pairs of 2-digit numbers that add to 100 to find related pairs that add to 100 or a number close to100 (for example, 20 + 80 = 100, so 22 + 78 = 100)
- Estimating the sums of 2-digit numbers by using knowledge of place value and known combinations
- Finding combinations of coins that equal $1.00
- Using mathematical tools (cubes, 100 charts and grids, number lines) to solve problems and represent strategies

Unit 3 Math Focus Points
- Estimating the sums of 2- and 3-digit numbers using knowledge of place value and known combinations
- Finding pairs of numbers that add to 100
- Finding the difference between 2- and 3-digit numbers and 100
- Finding the difference between 3-digit numbers
- Solving addition problems with 2- and 3-digit numbers (to 400) by breaking numbers apart and recombining them
- Representing addition strategies
- Adding and subtracting multiples of 10 and 100
- Developing strategies for solving addition problems by focusing on how each strategy starts

- Gaining fluency with subtraction facts related to addition combinations up to $10 + 10$
- Using multiples of 100 as a landmark to solve subtraction problems
- Solving subtraction problems with 2- and 3-digit numbers (to 300) using strategies that involve either subtracting one number in parts, adding up, or subtracting back
- Finding the difference between two numbers by either adding or subtracting
- Reasoning about how increasing the numbers in a subtraction problem affects the difference

Unit 8 Math Focus Points

- Combining hundreds to numbers above 1,000
- Subtracting from multiples of 100
- Adding multiples of 10 and 100 to, and subtracting them from, 3-digit numbers
- Estimating answers to subtraction problems with 3-digit numbers
- Using the relationship of numbers in a subtraction expression to multiples of 100 to solve subtraction problems
- Solving addition problems with 3-digit numbers
- Estimating and solving addition problems with sums greater than 1,000
- Solving addition problems with more than 2 addends
- Estimating which of two sums is greater
- Knowing and using subtraction problems related to the addition combinations to $10 + 10$ (the subtraction facts, e.g., $8 - 5$, $13 - 9$) with fluency
- Determining combinations of addends for a given sum
- Solving addition and subtraction problems with more than one step
- Solving addition and subtraction problems in the context of money (dollars, cents)

Whole Number Operations **Understanding different types of subtraction problems**

Unit 3 Math Focus Points

- Solving subtraction problems that involve finding a missing part
- Visualizing and representing the action of a subtraction problem which involves finding a missing part
- Understanding comparison as the difference between two numbers
- Solving subtraction story problems that involve comparison
- Visualizing and representing the action of comparison problems
- Using number lines to represent solutions to comparison problems
- Solving subtraction problems that involve removal
- Visualizing and representing the action of removal problems

Whole Number Operations **Understanding the meaning of multiplication**

Unit 5 Math Focus Points

- Understanding multiplication as combining equal groups
- Writing and solving multiplication problems in contexts
- Identifying the number of groups, the number in each group, and the product in a multiplication situation
- Understanding the relationship among skip counting, repeated addition, and multiplication
- Using and understanding multiplication notation

Whole Number Operations Reasoning about numbers and their factors and multiples

Unit 5 Math Focus Points

- Finding the multiples of the numbers 2, 3, 4, 5, 6, and 10 by skip counting
- Describing and comparing characteristics of the multiples of a number
- Understanding that doubling (or halving) one factor in a multiplication expression doubles (or halves) the product

Whole Number Operations Understanding and working with an array model of multiplication

Unit 5 Math Focus Points

- Using arrays to model multiplication situations
- Using arrays to find factors of 2-digit numbers up to 50
- Using arrays to identify characteristics of numbers, including prime and square numbers
- Using arrays to find a product by skip counting by one of its dimensions
- Breaking an array into parts to find the product represented by the array

Computational Fluency Learning the multiplication combinations with products up to 50 fluently

Unit 5 Math Focus Points

- Using known multiplication combinations to determine the product of more difficult combinations
- Identifying and learning multiplication combinations not yet known fluently

Unit 8 Math Focus Points

- Fluently solving multiplication combinations with products to 50

Whole Number Operations Developing strategies for division based on understanding the inverse relationship between multiplication and division

Unit 5 Math Focus Points

- Understanding division as the splitting of a quantity into equal groups
- Using the inverse relationship between multiplication and division to solve problems
- Using multiplication combinations to solve division problems
- Using and understanding division notation
- Writing and solving division problems in contexts

Whole Number Operations Describing, analyzing, and comparing strategies for adding and subtracting whole numbers

Unit 8 Math Focus Points

- Using story contexts and representations to support explanations about how changing a number in a subtraction problem affects the difference (e.g., $200 - 75 = 125$ and $200 - 78 = 122$)
- Solving addition problems by changing the numbers to create an equivalent problem that is easier to solve
- Using story contexts and representations to support explanations about equivalent addition expressions (e.g., $88 + 105 = 90 + 103$)
- Identifying addition strategies by focusing on how each strategy starts
- Solving subtraction problems that involve comparison, removal, or finding missing part
- Subtracting 3-digit numbers by using strategies that involve either subtracting one number in parts, adding up, or subtracting back
- Representing solutions to subtraction problems with number lines, 1,000 charts, and/or story contexts
- Subtracting by using strategies that involve changing one number to make a problem that is easier to solve

Rational Numbers **Understanding the meaning of fractions (halves, fourths, eighths, thirds, sixths) and decimal fractions (0.50, 0.25) as equal parts of a whole (an object, an area, a set of objects)**

Unit 7 Math Focus Points

- Finding equal parts of a whole and naming them with fractions
- Dividing an area into equal parts
- Naming fractional parts with unit fractions ($\frac{1}{2}, \frac{1}{3}, \frac{1}{4}$, etc.)
- Ordering unit fractions
- Demonstrating that different-shaped pieces that are the same fraction of the same area have equal areas
- Naming fractional parts with fractions that have numerators greater than 1 ($\frac{3}{4}, \frac{2}{3}, \frac{3}{6}$, etc.)
- Dividing a group into equal parts and naming the parts with fractions
- Using fraction notation to record equivalencies (e.g., $\frac{3}{6} = \frac{1}{2}, \frac{1}{2} = \frac{2}{4}$)
- Identifying equivalent fractional parts
- Using mixed numbers to represent quantities greater than 1
- Identifying equivalent fractions and decimals for values involving halves and fourths (e.g., $\frac{1}{2} = 0.50, \frac{1}{4} = 0.25, 2\frac{1}{2} = 2.5$)
- Reading, writing, and interpreting the meaning of the decimal numbers 0.50, 0.25, and numbers greater than 1 with these decimal portions, such as 2.5 and 2.25.

Rational Numbers **Using representations to combine fractions (halves, fourths, eighths, thirds, and sixths)**

Unit 7 Math Focus Points

- Using representations to combine fractions that sum to 1 (e.g., $\frac{1}{4} + \frac{3}{4} = 1, \frac{1}{3} + \frac{1}{3} + \frac{1}{3} = 1, \frac{1}{2} + \frac{1}{4} + \frac{1}{4} = 1$)
- Using representations to combine fractions to equal other fractions ($\frac{1}{2} = \frac{1}{3} + \frac{1}{6}$)

Patterns, Functions, and Change

Using Tables and Graphs **Using graphs to represent change**

Unit 6 Math Focus Points

- Describing the overall shape of a line graph—increasing, decreasing, staying the same
- Finding the difference between values on a line graph, including the difference between a positive and negative value
- Associating a story with its corresponding graph
- Plotting points on a graph to represent a situation in which one quantity is changing in relation to another
- Identifying points on a graph with corresponding values in a table and interpreting the numerical information in terms of the situation the graph represents
- Comparing situations by describing differences in their graphs

Using Tables and Graphs **Using tables to represent change**

Unit 6 Math Focus Points

- Using tables to represent the relationship between two quantities in a situation with a constant rate of change
- Interpreting numbers in a table in terms of the situation they represent
- Comparing situations by describing differences in the tables that represent them

Linear Change Describing and representing a constant rate change

Unit 6 Math Focus Points

- Describing the relationship between two quantities in a situation with a constant rate of change, taking into account a beginning amount and a constant increase
- Creating a representation for a situation with a constant rate of change
- Comparing different representations that show the same situation
- Making rules that relate one variable to the other in situations with a constant rate of change
- Connecting the steps of a general method or rule to the parts of the situation they represent

Number Sequences Constructing, describing, and extending number sequences with constant increments generated by various contexts

Unit 6 Math Focus Points

- Identifying the unit of a repeating pattern
- Associating counting numbers with elements of a pattern
- Determining the element of an ABC pattern associated with a particular counting number
- Describing and extending a number sequence with a constant increment (e.g., 3, 6, 9, . . . or 2, 5, 8, . . .)
- Identifying numbers that are multiples of three, or one less or one more than a multiple of 3

Data and Probability

Data Analysis Describing, summarizing, and comparing data

Unit 2 Math Focus Points

- Describing and interpreting categorical data
- Describing the shape of ordered, numerical data: where data are spread out or concentrated, where there are few data, highest and lowest values, and outliers
- Determining the range and mode of the data
- Using summaries such as *almost all*, *very few*, *half*, or *more than half*
- Describing what values are typical or atypical in a data set
- Developing arguments based on the data
- Using data to compare groups

Data Analysis Representing data

Unit 2 Math Focus Points

- Developing classifications to organize categorical data
- Organizing categorical data in different ways to answer different questions
- Representing categorical data using a picture or graph
- Reading and interpreting a bar graph
- Reading a scale on a graph with intervals larger than 1
- Using a line plot, bar graph, or other representation to represent ordered, numerical data
- Interpreting what the numbers and symbols on a line plot mean
- Developing a consistent scale to show where data are and are not concentrated
- Reading and interpreting a representation of ordered, numerical data
- Considering how well a data representation communicates to an audience

Data Analysis **Designing and carrying out a data investigation**

Unit 2 Math Focus Points

- Developing and revising a survey question
- Interpreting results of a data investigation

GRADE 3

Geometry

Features of Shape **Describing and classifying two-dimenstional figures**

Unit 4 Math Focus Points

- Determining the geometric moves needed (slides, flips, turns) to prove or disprove congruence between two shapes
- Identifying the attributes of triangles: three sides, three vertices, and three angles
- Identifying the attributes of quadrilaterals: four sides, four vertices, and four angles
- Comparing the properties of squares and rectangles

Features of Shape **Describing and measuring angles**

Unit 4 Math Focus Points

- Recognizing right angles
- Identifying a right angle as having a measure of 90 degrees
- Understanding angle size as the degree of turn
- Comparing the sizes of angles

Features of Shape **Describing properties of three-dimensional shapes**

Unit 9 Math Focus Points

- Describing the components and properties of different classes of solids such as polyhedra (3-D shapes having only flat surfaces, such as prisms and pyramids) and nonpolyhedra (such as cones and cylinders)
- Distinguishing between polyhedra and nonpolyhedra
- Distinguishing between prisms and pyramids
- Identifying the components of polyhedra (faces, edges, and vertices) and how they come together to form the whole
- Visualizing and building polyhedra by using knowledge of their components (faces, edges, and vertices) and how they come together to form the whole

Features of Shape **Translating between two-dimensional and three-dimensional shapes**

Unit 9 Math Focus Points

- Determining the number and shapes of the faces of cubes and other rectangular prisms and how they come together to form the whole
- Designing patterns that make open boxes for a cube
- Designing patterns that make open boxes for 2-cube rectangular prisms
- Designing patterns that make nets for triangular pyramids
- Determining the number and shapes of the faces of a triangular pyramid and how they come together to form the whole
- Communicating about spatial relationships
- Decomposing images of 3-D shapes and then recombining them to make a given structure

Measurement

Linear Measurement Measuring with standard units

Unit 2 Math Focus Points

◆ Measuring in inches
◆ Measuring lengths longer than the measuring tool
◆ Understanding the relationship between feet and inches
◆ Combining feet and inches to get a total measurement
◆ Using correct notation to write a measurement in feet and inches

Unit 4 Math Focus Points

◆ Reviewing the length of units of measure (inch, foot, yard, centimeter, and meter)
◆ Establishing measurement benchmarks
◆ Using U.S. standard and metric units to accurately measure length
◆ Recognizing and explaining possible sources of measurement error

Linear Measurement Understanding and finding perimeter

Unit 4 Math Focus Points

◆ Understanding perimeter as the measure around the outside edges of a two-dimensional figure
◆ Finding perimeter using standard units
◆ Creating different shapes with the same perimeter
◆ Finding the perimeter of an irregular shape

Area Measurement Understanding and finding area

Unit 4 Math Focus Points

◆ Understanding that area is measured in square units
◆ Understanding that when measuring area, the space being measured must be completely covered with no gaps or overlaps
◆ Using squares and triangles to make shapes with an area of four square units
◆ Examining the relationship between the area of squares and triangles
◆ Understanding that shapes with the same area can look different
◆ Finding the area of partially covered rectangles
◆ Finding the area of an irregular shape
◆ Designing a shape for a given area
◆ Finding area by counting or calculating whole and partial square units

Measuring Temperature Understanding temperature and measuring with standard units

Unit 6 Math Focus Points

◆ Reading and interpreting positive and negative temperatures on a thermometer and on a line graph
◆ Associating temperatures with particular activities or clothing

Volume Structuring rectangular prisms and determining their volume

Unit 9 Math Focus Points

◆ Determining the number of cubes that will fit in the box made by a given pattern
◆ Designing patterns for boxes that will hold a given number of cubes
◆ Seeing that the cubes filling a rectangular prism can be decomposed into congruent layers

GRADE 3

Classroom Routines

Class Collection

Unit 3 Math Focus Points

- Solving addition problems with 2- and 3-digit numbers
- Finding the difference between 3-digit numbers
- Finding the difference between 2- and 3-digit numbers and 1,000

What's the Temperature?

Units 1–9 Math Focus Points

- Learning about temperature: reading a thermometer, learning to associate different temperatures with words like *colder* and *warmer*, and establishing landmark temperatures
- Recording information in a table and on a graph
- Reading information from the shape of a graph: hot, cold, increasing, decreasing

GRADE 3

Ten-Minute Math

Counting Around the Class

Units 5 and 8 Math Focus Points

- Finding the multiples of numbers through skip counting
- Becoming familiar with multiplication patterns
- Understanding the relationship between skip counting and multiplication

Guess My Rule

Units 2, 6, and 8 Math Focus Points

- Using evidence and formulating questions to make hypotheses about the common characteristics of groups of people or things
- Systematically eliminating possibilities
- Using mathematical terms to describe numbers

More or Less?

Units 1, 2, and 9 Math Focus Points

- Breaking apart, reordering, or combining numbers within a problem, for easier computation
- Using knowledge of place value and known combinations to estimate sums and differences
- Practicing addition and subtraction skills

Practicing Place Value

Units 1 and 4 Math Focus Points

- Recognizing and interpreting the value of each digit in 2- and 3- digit numbers
- Finding different combinations of a number, using only 100s, 10s, and 1s and recognizing their equivalence (i.e. 1 hundred, 3 tens, and 7 ones = 1 hundred, 2 tens, and 17 ones = 13 tens and 7 ones = 12 tens and 17 ones, etc.)
- Reading and writing numbers up to 1,000
- Adding multiples of 10 to, and subtracting multiples of 10 from 2- and 3-digit numbers

Quick Images

Units 4 and 9 Math Focus Points

- Organizing and analyzing visual images
- Developing language and concepts needed to communicate about spatial relationships
- Decomposing images of 2-D shapes and then recombining them to make a given design (Unit 4)
- Decomposing images of 3-D shapes and then recombining them to make a given structure (Unit 9)

Today's Number

Units 2, 3, 6, and 7 Math Focus Points

- Generating equivalent expressions for a number using particular constraints
- Practicing computation skills
- Using notation to record expressions

What Time Is It?

Units 3, 5, and 7 Math Focus Points

- Naming, notating, and telling time to the nearest 5 minutes on a digital or analog clock
- Telling time to any minute on a digital or analog clock
- Determining intervals of time to the minute

GRADE 4

Number and Operations

Whole Number Operations Understanding and working with an array model of multiplication

Unit 1 Math Focus Points

- Using arrays to model multiplication situations
- Breaking an array into parts to find the product represented by the array
- Using arrays to find factors of 2-digit numbers
- Identifying features of numbers, including prime, square, and composite numbers

Whole Number Operations Reasoning about numbers and their factors

Unit 1 Math Focus Points

- Finding the multiples of a number by skip counting
- Determining whether one number is a factor or multiple of another
- Identifying the factors of a given number
- Identifying all the factors of 100
- Using knowledge of the factors of 100 to find factors of multiples of 100
- Using known multiplication combinations to find related multiplication combinations for a given product (e.g., if $4 \times 50 = 200$, then $8 \times 25 = 200$)
- Using representations to show that a factor of a number is also a factor of its multiples (e.g., if 25 is a factor of 100, then 25 is also a factor of 300)

Unit 3 Math Focus Points

◈ Understanding the effect of multiplying by a multiple of 10 (e.g., describing the relationship between 3×4 and 3×40)

◈ Finding multiples of 2-digit numbers

◈ Describing a sequence of multiples in order to predict other multiples

◈ Determining the effect on the product when a factor is doubled or halved

---

Whole Number Operations Understanding and using the relationship between multiplication and division to solve division problems

Unit 3 Math Focus Points

◈ Solving division story problems

◈ Using and interpreting division notation

◈ Solving division problems by making groups of the divisor

◈ Using known multiplication combinations to solve division problems

Unit 8 Math Focus Points

◈ Representing a multiplication or division problem with pictures or diagrams, including arrays and pictures of groups

◈ Using a story problem represented by a multiplication expression to keep track of parts of the problems

---

Whole Number Operations Describing, analyzing, and comparing strategies for adding and subtracting whole numbers

Unit 5 Math Focus Points

◈ Representing addition and subtraction on a number line

◈ Identifying, describing, and comparing addition and subtraction strategies by focusing on how each strategy starts

◈ Developing arguments about why two addition expressions are equivalent (e.g., $597 + 375 = 600 + 372$)

◈ Using story contexts and representations to support explanations about equivalent addition expressions

◈ Understanding the meaning of the steps and notation of the U.S. algorithm for addition

◈ Identifying, describing, and comparing subtraction strategies by focusing on how each strategy starts

◈ Developing arguments about how the differences represented by two subtraction expressions are related (e.g., $432 - 198$ and $432 - 200$)

◈ Using story contexts and representations to support explanations about related subtraction expressions

---

Whole Number Operations Understanding different types of subtraction problems

Unit 5 Math Focus Points

◈ Understanding the action of subtraction problems

◈ Representing subtraction situations

Whole Number Operations Representing the meaning of multiplication and division

Unit 3 Math Focus Points

◈ Representing a multiplication or division problem with pictures, diagrams, or models

◈ Using arrays to model multiplication

◈ Making sense of remainders in terms of the problem context

◈ Creating a story problem to represent a division expression

◈ Comparing visual representations of multiplication situations

Whole Number Operations **Understanding division as making groups of the divisor**

Unit 8 Math Focus Points

- Solving division problems by breaking the problem into parts
- Using multiples of 10 to solve division problems
- Using the relationship between multiplication and division to solve division problems

The Base-Ten Number System **Extending knowledge of the number system to 10,000**

Unit 5 Math Focus Points

- Reading, writing, and sequencing numbers to 1,000 and 10,000
- Understanding the structure of 10,000 and its equivalence to one thousand 10s, one hundred 100s, and ten 1,000s
- Recognizing the place value of digits in large numbers

Computational Fluency **Fluency with multiplication combinations to 12 × 12**

Unit 1 Math Focus Points

- Identifying and learning multiplication combinations not yet known fluently
- Using known multiplication combinations to determine the product of more difficult combinations

Computational Fluency **Solving multiplication problems with 2-digit numbers**

Unit 3 Math Focus Points

- Developing strategies for multiplying that involve breaking apart numbers
- Reviewing multiplication combinations to 12 × 12
- Multiplying multiples of 10

Unit 8 Math Focus Points

- Estimating solutions to 2-digit multiplication problems
- Multiplying multiples of 10
- Solving 2-digit multiplication problems by breaking a problem into smaller parts and combining the subproducts
- Solving 2-digit multiplication problems by changing one factor to create an easier problem

Computational Fluency **Adding and subtracting accurately and efficiently**

Unit 5 Math Focus Points

- Adding and subtracting multiples of 10, 100, and 1,000
- Using multiples of 10 and 100 to find the difference between any 3-digit number and 1,000
- Adding 3- and 4-digit numbers
- Using clear and concise notation for recording addition and subtraction strategies
- Finding combinations of 3-digit numbers that add to 1,000
- Solving subtraction problems by breaking numbers apart
- Solving multistep addition and subtraction problems
- Combining positive and negative numbers

Rational Numbers **Understanding the meaning of fractions and decimal fractions**

Unit 6 Math Focus Points

- Finding fractional parts of a rectangular area
- Finding fractional parts of a group (of objects, people, etc.)
- Interpreting the meaning of the numerator and the denominator of a fraction
- Writing, reading, and applying fraction notation
- Representing fractions greater than 1
- Identifying everyday uses of fractions and decimals
- Reading and writing tenths and hundredths
- Representing tenths and hundredths as parts of an area

Rational Numbers **Comparing the values of fractions and decimal fractions**

Unit 6 Math Focus Points

- Identifying relationships between unit fractions when one denominator is a multiple of the other (e.g., halves and fourths, thirds and sixths)
- Comparing the same fractional parts of different-sized wholes
- Identifying equivalent fractions
- Ordering fractions and justifying their order through reasoning about fraction equivalencies and relationships
- Representing fractions using a number line
- Comparing fractions to the landmarks $0, \frac{1}{2}, 1$, and 2
- Ordering decimals and justifying their order through reasoning about representations and meaning of the numbers
- Identifying decimal and fraction equivalents

Computation with Rational Numbers **Using representations to add rational numbers**

Unit 6 Math Focus Points

- Using representations to add fractions that sum to 1
- Estimating sums of fractions
- Adding fractions with the same and related denominators (e.g., halves, fourths, and eighths; thirds and sixths)
- Estimating sums of decimal numbers
- Adding decimal numbers that are multiples of 0.1 and 0.25 (e.g., $2.3 + 3.25$)
- Using representations to combine tenths and hundredths

GRADE 4

Patterns, Functions, and Change

Using Tables and Graphs **Using graphs to represent change**

Unit 9 Math Focus Points

- Interpreting the points and shape of a graph in terms of the situation the graph represents
- Finding the difference between two values on a line graph
- Discriminating between features of a graph that represent quantity and those that represent changes in quantity
- Plotting points on a coordinate grid to represent a situation in which one quantity is changing in relation to another
- Identifying points in a graph with corresponding values in a table and interpreting the numerical information in terms of the situation the graph represents
- Comparing situations by describing differences in their graphs
- Describing the relative steepness of graphs or parts of graphs in terms of different rates of change
- Comparing tables, graphs, and situations of constant change with those of non-constant change

Using Tables and Graphs **Using tables to represent change**

Unit 9 Math Focus Points

- Interpreting numbers in a table in terms of the situation they represent
- Using tables to represent the relationship between two quantities in a situation of constant change

Linear Change **Describing and representing a constant rate of change**

Unit 9 Math Focus Points

- Describing the relationship between two quantities in a situation of constant change, taking into account a beginning amount and a constant increase
- Creating a representation for a situation of constant change
- Finding the value of one quantity in a situation of constant change, given the value of the other
- Writing an arithmetic expression for finding the value of one quantity in terms of the other in a situation of constant change
- Making rules that relate one variable to another in situations of constant change
- Using symbolic letter notation to represent the value of one variable in terms of another

Data and Probability

Data Analysis **Representing Data**

Unit 2 Math Focus Points

- Organizing ordered numerical data to describe a data set
- Using a line plot to represent ordered numerical data
- Representing two sets of data in order to compare them

Data Analysis **Describing, summarizing, and comparing data**

Unit 2 Math Focus Points

- Describing the shape of a data set: where the data are spread out or concentrated, what the highest and lowest values are, what the range is, and what the outliers are
- Determining the range of a data set
- Describing and interpreting data that compare two groups
- Describing what values are typical or atypical in a data set
- Comparing two sets of data using the shape and spread of the data
- Finding the median of a data set
- Using medians to compare groups
- Considering what information a median does and does not provide

Data Analysis **Analyzing and interpreting data**

Unit 2 Math Focus Points

- Drawing conclusions based on data
- Developing arguments based on the data

Data Analysis Designing and carrying out a data investigation

Unit 2 Math Focus Points

- Recording and keeping track of data
- Considering how well a data representation communicates to an audience
- Developing and revising a survey question

Probability Describing the probability of an event

Unit 2 Math Focus Points

- Associating the word probability with the likelihood of an event
- Arranging events along a line representing the range of certain to impossible
- Associating verbal descriptions of probability with numeric descriptions
- Using numbers from 0 to 1 as measures of probability
- Comparing the expected probability of an event with the actual results of repeated trials of that event

GRADE 4

Geometry

Features of Shape Describing and classifying two-dimensional figures

Unit 4 Math Focus Points

- Defining polygons as closed figures with line segments as sides and vertices
- Classifying polygons by attribute, including number of sides, length of sides, and size of angles
- Combining polygons to make new polygons
- Recognizing number of sides as a descriptor of various polygons
- Developing vocabulary to describe attributes and properties of quadrilaterals
- Understanding the relationship between squares and rectangles
- Making designs with mirror symmetry

Features of Shape Describing and measuring angles

Unit 4 Math Focus Points

- Identifying a right angle as 90 degrees
- Measuring acute angles by relating them to 90 degrees
- Using known angles to find the measure of other angles

Features of Shape Describing properties of three-dimensional shapes

Unit 7 Math Focus Points

- Describing attributes of geometric solids
- Naming geometric solids

Features of Shape Translating between two-dimensional and three-dimensional shapes

Unit 7 Math Focus Points

- Understanding how 3-D solids project silhouettes with 2-D shapes (for example, how a cone can produce both triangular and circular silhouettes)
- Decomposing images of 3-D shapes and then recombining them to make a given structure
- Visualizing what 3-D figures look like from different perspectives
- Recognizing how components of 3-D cube buildings come together to form the whole building
- Drawing silhouettes of 3-D cube buildings from different perspectives
- Integrating different silhouettes of an object, both to form a mental model and to build the whole object

GRADE 4

Measurement

Linear Measurement Measuring with standard units

Unit 4 Math Focus Points

- Reviewing the lengths of units of measure (inches, feet, yards, centimeters, meters)
- Using U.S. standard and metric units to accurately measure length
- Estimating lengths based on common units (centimeter, inch, foot, yard, meter)
- Determining when estimates or exact measurements are needed
- Finding perimeter using standard units
- Recognizing and explaining possible sources of measurement error
- Comparing different paths that have the same length

Unit 9 Math Focus Points

- Measuring in centimeters

Area Measurement Finding and understanding area

Unit 4 Math Focus Points

- Finding the area of symmetrical designs
- Understanding that the larger the unit of area, the smaller the number of units needed to measure the area
- Dividing irregular polygons into two shapes that have equal area
- Finding the area of polygons by decomposing shapes
- Finding the area of polygons using square units
- Finding the area of rectangles
- Finding the area of triangles in relation to the area of rectangles

Volume Structuring rectangular prisms and determining their volume

Unit 7 Math Focus Points

- Seeing that cubes filling a rectangular prism can be decomposed into congruent layers
- Finding the volume of cube buildings
- Designing patterns for boxes that hold a given number of cubes (volume)
- Developing a strategy for determining the volume of rectangular prisms
- Finding the number of cubes (volume) that will fit into the box made by a given pattern
- Doubling the number of cubes for a given box and considering how that changes the dimensions of the original box

Ten-Minute Math

Closest Estimate

Units 8 and 9 Math Focus Points

- Approximating numbers to nearby landmark numbers (e.g., multiples of 10 or 100)
- Calculating mentally
- Comparing answer choices to find the one closest to the actual answer

Counting Around the Class

Units 1, 3, and 8 Math Focus Points

- Finding the multiples of numbers through skip counting
- Becoming familiar with multiplication patterns
- Understanding the relationship between skip counting and multiplication

Practicing Place Value

Units 5, 6, and 7 Math Focus Points

- Recognizing and interpreting the value of each digit in 3- and 4-digit numbers
- Reading and writing numbers up to 10,000
- Adding multiples of 10 to, and subtracting multiples of 10 from 3- and 4-digit numbers
- Reading and writing decimal fractions and decimal numbers
- Adding tenths to, and subtracting them from, decimal fractions and decimal numbers

Quick Images

Units 1, 4, and 7 Math Focus Points

- Organizing and analyzing visual images
- Developing language and concepts needed to communicate about spatial relationships
- Writing equations to describe shape patterns (Unit 1)
- Decomposing images of 2-D shapes and then recombining them to make a given design (Unit 4)
- Decomposing images of 3-D shapes and then recombining them to make a given structure (Unit 7)

Quick Survey

Units 2, 6, and 9 Math Focus Points

- Describing features of the data
- Interpreting a set of data

Today's Number

Units 1, 2, 4, and 5 Math Focus Points

- Generating equivalent expressions for a number using particular constraints
- Practicing computation skills
- Using notation to record expressions

NCTM Curriculum Focal Points and Connections

The set of three curriculum focal points and related connections for mathematics in grade 3 follow. These topics are the recommended content emphases for this grade level. It is essential that these focal points be addressed in contexts that promote problem solving, reasoning, communication, making connections, and designing and analyzing representations.

Grade 3 Curriculum Focal Points	Investigations Units
Number and Operations and ***Algebra:*** **Developing understandings of multiplication and division and strategies for basic multiplication facts and related division facts** Students understand the meanings of multiplication and division of whole numbers through the use of representations (e.g., equal-sized groups, arrays, area models, and equal "jumps" on number lines for multiplication, and successive subtraction, partitioning, and sharing for division). They use properties of addition and multiplication (e.g., commutativity, associativity, and the distributive property) to multiply whole numbers and apply increasingly sophisticated strategies based on these properties to solve multiplication and division problems involving basic facts. By comparing a variety of solution strategies, students relate multiplication and division as inverse operations.	**Addressed in the work of:** • *Equal Groups* (Multiplication and Division) • *Stories, Tables, and Graphs* (Patterns, Functions, and Change) • Ten-Minute Math: *Counting Around the Class, Today's Number* **Also supported in the work of:** • *Surveys and Line Plots* (Data Analysis) • *Solids and Boxes* (3-D Geometry and Measurement)
Number and Operations: **Developing an understanding of fractions and fraction equivalence** Students develop an understanding of the meanings and uses of fractions to represent parts of a whole, parts of a set, or points or distances on a number line. They understand that the size of a fractional part is relative to the size of the whole, and they use fractions to represent numbers that are equal to, less than, or greater than 1. They solve problems that involve comparing and ordering fractions by using models, benchmark fractions, or common numerators or denominators. They understand and use models, including the number line, to identify equivalent fractions.	**Addressed in the work of:** • *Finding Fair Shares* (Fractions and Decimals) • Ten-Minute Math: *Guess My Rule* **Also supported in the work of:** • *Surveys and Line Plots* (Data Analysis)
Geometry: **Describing and analyzing properties of two-dimensional shapes** Students describe, analyze, compare, and classify two-dimensional shapes by their sides and angles and connect these attributes to definitions of shapes. Students investigate, describe, and reason about decomposing, combining, and transforming polygons to make other polygons. Through building, drawing, and analyzing two-dimensional shapes, students understand attributes and properties of two-dimensional space and the use of those attributes and properties in solving problems, including applications involving congruence and symmetry.	**Addressed in the work of:** • *Perimeter, Angles, and Area* (2-D Geometry and Measurement) • Ten-Minute Math: *Quick Images: 2D* **Also supported in the work of:** • *Solids and Boxes* (3-D Geometry and Measurement) • Technology: *LogoPaths* Software

Connections to the Focal Points	*Investigations* Units
Algebra: Understanding properties of multiplication and the relationship between multiplication and division is a part of algebra readiness that develops at grade 3. The creation and analysis of patterns and relationships involving multiplication and division should occur at this grade level. Students build a foundation for later understanding of functional relationships by describing relationships in context with such statements as, "The number of legs is 4 times the number of chairs."	**Addressed in the work of:** • *Stories, Tables, and Graphs* (Patterns, Functions, and Change) • *Equal Groups* (Multiplication and Division) • Classroom Routine: *What's The Temperature?, Class Collections* • Ten-Minute Math: *Counting Around The Class, Today's Number*
Measurement: Students in grade 3 strengthen their understanding of fractions as they confront problems in linear measurement that call for more precision than the whole unit allowed them in their work in grade 2. They develop their facility in measuring with fractional parts of linear units. Students develop measurement concepts and skills through experiences in analyzing attributes and properties of two-dimensional objects. They form an understanding of perimeter as a measurable attribute and select appropriate units, strategies, and tools to solve problems involving perimeter.	**Addressed in the work of:** • *Perimeter, Angles, and Area* (2-D Geometry and Measurement) • Technology: *LogoPaths* Software **Also supported in the work of:** • *Surveys and Line Plots* (Data Analysis) • *Finding Fair Shares* (Fractions and Decimals)
Data Analysis: Addition, subtraction, multiplication, and division of whole numbers come into play as students construct and analyze frequency tables, bar graphs, picture graphs, and line plots and use them to solve problems.	**Addressed in the work of:** • *Surveys and Line Plots* (Data Analysis) • Ten-Minute Math: *Guess My Rule*
Number and Operations: Building on their work in grade 2, students extend their understanding of place value to numbers up to 10,000 in various contexts. Students also apply this understanding to the task of representing numbers in different equivalent forms (e.g., expanded notation). They develop their understanding of numbers by building their facility with mental computation (addition and subtraction in special cases, such as 2,500 + 6,000 and 9,000 − 5,000), by using computational estimation, and by performing paper-and-pencil computations.	**Addressed in the work of:** • *Trading Stickers, Combining Coins* (Addition, Subtraction, and the Number System 1) • *Collections and Travel Stories* (Addition, Subtraction, and the Number System 2) • *How Many Hundreds? How Many Miles?* (Addition, Subtraction, and the Number System 3) • Classroom Routine: *Class Collections* • Ten-Minute Math: *Practicing Place Value, Today's Number, More or Less*

Each entry is identified by the Curriculum Unit number (in yellow) and its page number(s).

A

Addends. *See also* Addition.
   with a given sum, U8: 138–139, 143–144
   order of, U1: 41, 47, 115, 152; U3: 18–19;
      U8: 38, 87, 93–94, 156
Adding by place strategy, U1: 16, 45–46,
   126–128, 149–150, 153, 164
Adding one number in parts strategy,
   U1: 16–17, 46–48, 128–130, 150–151,
   154, 165
Adding up strategy, U3: 158–159, 161,
   164–165, 185–186, 210, 224;
   U8: 12–13, 17–19, 32, 112–115, 135,
   138–141, 163
Addition. *See also* Addends; Sum.
   of 10s and 1s, U1: 40–42, 61–64, 68–70
   to 100, U1: 122–123, 166–167
   associative property, U3: 18–19; U8: 155
   combinations, U1: 97–101, 122–123,
      159–163; U3: 109–111, 202
   commutative property, U3: 18–19
   comparison problems, U3: 157–162,
      164–165, 170–172, 174, 180, 223–224
   doubling, U1: 163
   of fractions, U7: 12, 39–42, 64–68, 83–86
   with a given sum, U8: 138–139, 143–145
   money problems, U8: 138–141, 143–145
   with more than ten ones, U1: 48–50
   with more than two addends, U8: 12,
      86–87, 92–95
   of multiples of 10, U1: 31–33, 37–39,
      72–74, 170; U3: 97–98
   multistep problems, U8: 12, 138–141,
      143–145
   notation for, U3: 73; U8: 12
   order of addends, U1: 41, 47, 115, 152;
      U3: 18–19; U8: 38, 87, 93–94, 155
   order of operations, U1: 61
   related problems, U3: 173, 180
   relationship to subtraction, U1: 57; U3: 18;
      U8: 12–13, 32–33, 163
   representations of, U1: 147–148;
      U3: 14, 69–70, 74, 78–79, 95,
      193–194; U8: 66–70
   starter problems, U3: 91–93, 96,
      101–102; U8: 73–76, 81–82
   story problems, U1: 45–48, 123; U3: 86
   strategies for, U1: 16–17, 45–48, 99,
      126–130, 149–151, 153–154, 164–166;
      U3: 14, 72–74, 78–79, 88–89, 101, 149,
      185–186, 195–197, 210, 219–220;
      U8: 10–13, 16–19, 37–39, 45–53,
      58–60, 65–71, 92–94

   with sums over 1,000, U8: 77–78
   of three-digit numbers, U3: 14, 41–43, 50,
      55, 58–61, 72–74, 76–78, 81–82, 87,
      95–96, 100–101, 137
   travel problems, U3: 129–135, 148–151;
      U8: 110–115
   of two-digit numbers, U3: 14, 41–43,
      50, 55, 61, 87, 95–96, 100–101, 137,
      157–162, 164–165, 170–172, 174, 180,
      223–224
   using 100 as a landmark for, U3: 116–120,
      123–127, 139, 143, 174, 181, 221–222
   using multiples of 10 and 100,
      U3: 13–14, 69–72
   U.S. Standard Algorithm, U8: 84
Angles
   acute, U4: 126, 131–133
   in the environment, U4: 126–128,
      131–133
   independence from size of figure, U4: 13,
      124–126, 132–133
   measurement by comparison,
      U4: 12–13, 131–133
   obtuse, U4: 125–126, 131–133
   of quadrilaterals, U4: 117, 120, 124–125
   right (90º), U4: 12–13, 79–80, 85,
      108–109, 120–122, 124–126, 131–133
   of triangles, U4: 107–109, 112–113
Area
   different shapes with same area,
      U4: 63–67, 85–87
   of irregular shapes, U4: 89–92, 96–97,
      156–157
   measurement of, U4: 11, 69–73, 84
   of rectangles, U4: 87, 90, 93, 96
   same perimeter/different area,
      U4: 79–80, 84, 90, 96
   of squares, U4: 155
   of triangles, U4: 144, 155
   units of measure for, U4: 75
Arrays
   congruent pairs of, U5: 84
   finding number of squares in, U5: 174
   modeling multiplication, U5: 11–12,
      16, 83–86, 89–91, 93–95, 100, 146,
      157–159, 173
   modeling strategies, U5: 158
Associative property of addition,
   U1: 152; U3: 18–19; U8: 155
Associative property of multiplication,
   U5: 16, 40, 72
Attributes
   of parallelograms, U4: 124–125
   of polygons, U4: 12–13

   of quadrilaterals, U4: 12, 117
   of rectangles, U4: 120–122
   of squares, U4: 120–122
   of triangles, U4: 12, 108–109, 112–113,
      158–159

B

Base-ten number system. *See also* Place
   value. U1: 10–11, 27–31, 143–144;
   U3: 12–13, 29–33, 191–192
Body movement patterns, U6: 57–58
Boxes
   closed box pattern, U9: 61–63, 109–110
   open, U9: 10–11, 51–54, 56–58, 60–61,
      71–73, 75–79, 81–84, 86–90, 100, 111
Breaking numbers apart strategy, U1: 16,
   45–48, 126–130, 149–151, 153–154,
   164–165; U3: 14, 72–74, 78–79, 88–89,
   101, 149, 185–186, 195–196, 210,
   219–220; U5: 12, 16, 66, 77–78, 94–95,
   102–103, 146, 158; U8: 11, 32–33, 42,
   82–84, 86, 92–93, 118–122, 124, 135,
   152–153, 163

C

Categorical data. *See* Data.
Categories, U2: 26–27, 69–72, 84, 159–160
**Changing numbers to make an easier
   problem strategy,** U1: 151; U3: 14,
   197, 210–211; U8: 65–71, 82–84, 124,
   129–130, 154–155, 164
Circles, U4: 51
Commutative property of addition,
   U1: 152; U3: 18–19
**Commutative property of
   multiplication,** U5: 12, 16, 85
Comparing, U8: 160–161
   different rates of increase/different
      starting amounts, U6: 12, 87, 93–94,
      106–107, 109–111, 148–149, 152–154
   different rates of increase/same starting
      amounts, U6: 94–96, 104–106,
      152–154
   with double bar graphs, U2: 51–54
   frequencies (data), U2: 12
   groups
      of categorical data, U2: 11–12,
         51–54, 64–67, 74–76, 185–186
      of numerical data, U2: 169
   multiples of 3 and 6, U5: 66–70, 72–73
   patterns of multiples on 100 Chart,
      U5: 152–153

related multiplication problems, U5: 60–62, 65–66

representations of change, U6: 83–84

same rate of increase/different starting amounts, U6: 89–91, 152–154

sums, U8: 103–108, 160–161

temperature graphs, U6: 13, 29–30

Comparison problems, U3: 157–162, 164–167, 170–172, 174, 180, 183–185, 203–204, 223–224; U8: 103–108, 119, 160–161

Cone, U9: 25–26, 95

Congruence, U4: 12, 65, 108–109

Constant rate of change comparing, U6: 87, 89–91, 93–94, 104–107, 109–111, 148–149, 152–154

graphs of, U6: 10–12, 16, 101, 104–107, 110–111, 130–133, 152–154

rules for, U6: 13, 17, 89–91, 94–96, 98–99, 125, 150–151

students' representations of, U6: 81–84

symbolic notation for, U6: 17, 99

tables of, U6: 86–91, 93–96, 100–102, 128–129, 148–149, 152-154

Counting all strategy, U4: 93; U5: 93

Counting back strategy, U8: 51

Counting by groups, U5: 152–154

of 2, U5: 49–50

of 3 and 6, U5: 56–58, 171–172

of 5 and 10, U5: 51–52, 54–55, 152–153, 170

Counting up strategy, U8: 51, 124

Cubes, U9: 43–45, 51–54, 56–57, 95, 109–110

Cylinders, U9: 25–26, 95

D

Data

analyzing, U2: 10–12

categorizing, U2: 10, 69–71

classifying, U2: 26–27, 29–31, 159–160

collecting, U2: 13

categorical data, U2: 13, 25–26, 32, 57–58, 60, 87–88, 103–104, 157–158

numerical data, U2: 13, 57–58, 60, 64, 83, 103–104, 127–130, 134–138, 144–146, 149, 162–163

comparing groups of categorical data, U2: 11–12, 51–54, 64–67, 69–71, 74–76, 185–186

definition, U2: 25, 159

describing

categorical data, U2: 11, 160–161, 163, 167

numerical data, U2: 11, 84–86, 110–111, 130–131, 146–147, 150–153, 163, 166–167

finding and using the median, U2: 170

frequencies of, U2: 11–12

interpreting, U2: 28, 37, 44–48, 50–51, 59–61, 64

landmarks of, U2: 11

measurements as, U2: 125–131

ordering by value, U2: 11, 84, 168

organizing categorical data, U2: 26–27, 29–31, 34–38, 43, 69–71, 157, 159–160

presenting projects, U2: 118–119

representations

of categorical data, U2: 12, 27–28, 37, 43–48, 71–72, 75

of numerical data, U2: 12, 50–51, 83–86, 92, 103–105, 108–112, 150–151, 163, 168–169

shape of graphs, U2: 12–13, 163–165

solving problems with, U2: 90–96

summarizing, U2: 64–67, 69–71, 74–76, 92–96

terms of, U2: 166–167

Decimal fractions, U7: 10–11, 92–94, 97–102, 104–105

Decimal point, U7: 94

Degrees, U4: 42–44, 48–49, 114, 121

Denominator, U7: 11, 25, 28

Difference. *See also* Subtraction. U1: 40; U3: 117–118, 138–140, 157–162, 164–167; U8: 103–108, 131, 160–161

Dimensions of arrays, U5: 83–86, 95, 100, 157–159, 173–174

Distance, U2: 126

Distributive property of multiplication, U5: 12, 16–17, 102

Division. *See also* Factors.

grouping problems, U5: 13

notation for, U5: 13, 123, 134, 148

related problems, U5: 126–128, 135, 138–139

relationship to multiplication, U5: 13, 16–17, 117, 119, 122–124, 148, 158, 175

sharing problems, U5: 12

story problems, U5: 117–119, 122

strategies for, U5: 119, 139–140

types of situations, U5: 12, 163–164

Division notation, U7: 94

Dollars, U7: 94–95, 126

Doubling, U6: 72, 124

Doubling and halving strategy, U1: 163; U3: 30; U5: 11, 16, 40, 55, 66–70, 72–73, 94–95, 152–153, 170–172

Grade 3 Curriculum Units

U1 Trading Stickers, Combining Coins

U2 Surveys and Line Plots

U3 Collections and Travel Stories

U4 Perimeter, Angles, and Area

U5 Equal Groups

U6 Stories, Tables, and Graphs

U7 Finding Fair Shares

U8 How Many Hundreds? How Many Miles?

U9 Solids and Boxes

E

Edges, U9: 26, 43–45, 95, 108

Eighths, U7: 10–12, 32–34, 39, 113

Equations, U1: 37, 77–78; U3: 82, 111, 117–118, 121, 149, 158–159; U5: 31–33; U7: 64–65, 75–76; U8: 66–67, 124

Equivalent expressions, U8: 56–58, 65–71, 154, 178

Equivalent problems strategy, U3: 197; U8: 12–13, 57, 65–71

Estimation, U1: 18, 109–112, 116, 121, 125, 133, 139; U3: 55–56, 76–78; U4: 25–28; U6: 29; U7: 48; U8: 10–11, 41–46, 73, 86, 106–108, 110–111

Even numbers, U5: 50

F

Faces, U9: 26, 30–31, 33, 35, 43–45, 51–58, 60–61, 75–79, 86–87, 95

Factors. *See also* Multiples; Multiplication combinations.

of 12, U5: 83–86, 94, 173

dimensions of arrays as, U5: 11–12, 16, 83–86, 88–91, 93–95, 100, 157–159, 173

finding all possible, U5: 83–86, 95, 100, 173

relationship to products, U5: 10

Figure. *See also* Non-Polyhedron; Polyhedron; Three-dimensional shapes. U9: 38

Flips, U4: 12, 65, 76, 86, 143

Fourths, U7: 10–12, 32–34, 37–39, 44, 48–52, 66–67, 91–94, 97–102, 104–105, 111–112

Fractions. *See also* Eighths; Fourths; Halves; Sixths; Thirds.

of 12, U7: 44–46

adding equivalents, U7: 39–42

combining, U7: 12

decimal equivalents, U7: 11, 92–94, 97–102, 104–105

developing meaning for, U7: 109–110

different shapes of same amount, U7: 25, 34

equal to 1, U7: 39–42, 63–65, 70–73, 79, 85–86

equations with, U7: 64–65, 75–76

equivalents, U7: 11, 50–51, 63–68, 72–73, 76–79, 81–86, 113–114, 123

greater than 1, U7: 48–51

notation for, U7: 38–39, 72–73

with numerators greater than 1, U7: 37–39, 55

ordering, U7: 32–34

relationship to whole, U7: 10–11

of a set of objects, U7: 44–46, 54–56

of a whole, U7: 10, 25–28, 30–34, 37–42

Frequencies. *See* Data.

G

Generalizations, U3: 19, 111; U5: 16–17; U8: 18–19, 57–58, 66–71, 168–170

Geometric motions, U4: 12, 64–65, 76, 86, 143

Geometric solids. *See* Three-dimensional shapes.

Geometry. *See* Area; Perimeter; Polygons; Three-dimensional shapes; Two-dimensional shapes.

Gestures, U6: 34, 42, 105

Graphs
  associating with corresponding stories, U6: 37–38, 45–47, 49–50

  bar, U2: 27, 50–54, 59–61, 64, 104–105, 108–109

  double bar, U2: 12, 51–54, 59–61, 109

  line
    associating with corresponding stories, U6: 37–38, 45–47, 49–50

    comparing situations with, U6: 106–107, 109–111, 152–154

    of constant rate of change with starting amount, U6: 10–12, 16, 101, 104–107, 109–111, 130–133, 152–154

    conventions of, U6: 117–118

    creating from tables, U6: 10–13, 100–102, 104–106

    describing/interpreting, U6: 25–31, 33–37, 40–41, 104–107, 110–111, 118, 142

    finding range, U6: 33–41

    horizontal axis, U6: 10, 42–43, 100, 118

    identifying points with corresponding values, U6: 104–105

    negative values on, U6: 33–37, 40–41

    representing change, U6: 117–118

    shape of, U6: 33–38

    of temperatures, U6: 10, 13, 26, 27–30, 33–38, 40–43, 45–47, 48, 49–51, 117, 119–123, 132–133, 142–143

    vertical axis, U6: 10, 30, 42–43, 100, 118

  line plots, U2: 12, 83–86, 90–92, 104–105, 108–109, 130–131, U6: 117

  terminology of, U6: 34, 41, 42, 45

Grouping problems, U5: 13, 117–119, 123, 163–164

Groups, U5: 25–27, 29–33, 36–38

Groups of divisor strategy, U5: 119

Groups of the denominator strategy, U7: 53

H

Halves
  equivalent decimals, U7: 97–102, 104–105

  equivalent fractions, U7: 66–68, 97–102, 104–105, 113–114

  ordering, U7: 32–34

  relationship to fourths and eighths, U7: 12, 113

  relationship to thirds and sixths, U7: 12, 63–68, 70, 72–73, 113–114

  of twelve, U7: 44–46

  of a whole, U7: 10, 25–27

Heights, U3: 161–162, 164–167

Hemisphere, U9: 25–26, 95

Hexagonal prism, U9: 95

Hexagonal pyramid, U9: 43–46

Hexagons, U7: 61–62, 70–73

Horizontal axis, U6: 10, 42–43, 100, 118

I

Irregular shapes, U4: 11, 89–92, 96, 155–156

J

Justification, U3: 19; U5: 16–17; U8: 18–19, 57–58, 66–71, 168–170

"Just knew" strategy, U3: 30

K

Known combinations strategy, U3: 30, 42–43, 55–56, 89; U5: 12, 16–17, 40, 66, 77–78, 94–95, 102–103, 108–110, 119, 123, 139–140; U7: 75–76; U8: 32–33, 92–93

L

Landmark numbers strategy, U3: 197

Landmarks
  of angles, U4: 126

  numbers, U1: 151; U3: 12, 30–32, 116–120, 123–127, 131–135, 139, 143, 174, 176–179, 181, 192, 197, 221–222; U8: 112–115

Landmark temperatures, U6: 26, 30

Length, U2: 13, 125; U3: 157–162, 164–167; U4: 10, 25, 30–36, 38–39

Linear functions. *See also* Constant rate of change. U6: 11–12, 16–17

Linear measure. *See* Length; Measurement; Perimeter.

***LogoPaths* Software,** U2: 13; U5: 13; U8: 13; U9: 11

  200 Steps, U4: 79–80, 84

  400 Steps, U4: 90

  500 Steps, U4: 96

  commands for, U4: 140–141

  Feed the Turtle, U4: 113–115, 119, 131

  introducing and managing, U4: 13, 139–141

  mathematics of, U4: 142

  Missing Measures, U4: 42–44, 48–49, 53

  saving student work on, U4: 141

  turtle turner and ruler tools, U4: 114

M

Maximum value, U6: 25, 29, 33–37, 40–41

Measurement
  accuracy of, U2: 13, 130, 138–140, 149, 192

  of area of rectangle, U4: 69–73

  concepts of, U4: 10

  as data, U2: 125–127

  of distances, U2: 133–134, 138–139, 144–145, 149

  equivalents, U2: 13, 133, 142–143

  estimation, U4: 25–28

  guidelines for, U2: 127, 139–140

  of feet, U2: 127–128

  of irregular shape, U2: 127–128; U4: 89–92, 96

  of length, U2: 125–127, 129–130, 136–138, 145–146, 149–153; U4: 25, 30–36, 38–39

  in more than one unit, U4: 33–34, 38–39

  of perimeter, U4: 30–36, 38–39

  techniques for, U4: 10, 32–34, 38–39, 138

  tools for, U4: 10, 23–24

Measurement benchmarks, U4: 13, 26, 126

Median, U2: 13, 94, 166–167, 170

Metric system. *See* Units of measure.

Minimum value, U6: 25, 29, 33–37, 40–41

Missing parts problems, U3: 129–135, 148–151, 157–162, 164–167, 183–184; **U5:** 130–132, 135, 138, 148; **U8:** 11–12, 110–115, 119, 161

Mode, U2: 11, 44, 66, 85–86, 164, 166–167

Money, U3: 71
    addition and subtraction of, **U1:** 117–120; **U8:** 12–13, 124–127, 129–131, 138–141
    converting to decimals and fractions, **U7:** 94–95, 123
    notation for, **U7:** 92, 94, 97
    problems with two steps, **U8:** 138–141, 143–145
    representing place value, **U1:** 11, 69, 117–120, 162; **U7:** 93–95

Multiples. *See also* Multiplication combinations. **U5:** 25–27
    of 1 or 2 less than 3, **U6:** 63–66, 68–72, 124–125
    of 2, **U5:** 49–50, 161
    of 3 and 6, **U5:** 56–58, 66–70, 72–73, 161, 171–172, of 3 and 6, **U6:** 24, 63–66, 68–72, 124–125
    of 4, **U5:** 161, of 4, **U6:** 103
    of 5 and 10, **U5:** 51–52, 54–55, 161, 170, 172, of 5 and 10, **U6:** 32, 44
    of 7, **U5:** 161–162
    of 8 and 9, **U5:** 161–162
    of 10, **U8:** 11, 37–39, 41–46, 56–60
    of 11, **U5:** 161–162
    of 12, **U5:** 161–162
    of 100, **U8:** 11, 31–35, 37–39, 41–46, 56–60, 112–115
    of prime numbers, **U5:** 88–89
    relationships between, **U5:** 11, 51–52, 54–55, 152–153, 171–172
    representations of, **U5:** 66–70, 72–73, 83–86, 88–91, 100, 173
    skip counting, **U5:** 50–52, 54–58, 152–153
    of square numbers, **U5:** 88, 161

Multiplication. *See also* Multiples; Multiplication combinations; Products.
    by 2, **U5:** 49–50
    associative property of, **U5:** 16, 40, 72
    commutative property of, **U5:** 12, 16, 85
    distributive property of, **U5:** 12, 16–17, 102
    notation for, **U5:** 10, 31–33, 134, 148
    prime numbers, **U5:** 88–89
    related problems, **U5:** 60–62, 65–66, 126–128, 135, 138–139
    relationship to division, **U5:** 13, 16–17, 117, 119, 122–124, 148, 158, 175
    representations of, **U5:** 16, 26, 29–33, 145–148, 157–159
    as skip counting/repeated addition, **U5:** 31, 36–38

square numbers, **U5:** 88
starter problems, **U5:** 77–78, 102–103
story problems, **U5:** 122
strategies for, **U5:** 12, 16–17, 25, 31, 40, 65–66, 77–78, 93–95, 98–99, 102–103, 108–110
use of in division problems, **U5:** 13, 16–17

Multiplication combinations, U5: 12; **U8:** 53–54, 149–151
    of 0, **U5:** 103, 161
    of 1, **U5:** 161
    of 2, **U5:** 49–50
    of 3 and 6, **U5:** 56–58, 66–70, 161, 171–172
    of 4, **U5:** 161
    of 5 and 10, **U5:** 51–52, 54–55, 161, 170, 172
    of 7, **U5:** 161–162
    of 8 and 9, **U5:** 161–162
    of 10, **U8:** 11, 31–35, 37–39, 41–46, 56–60, 112–115
    of 11, **U5:** 161–162
    of 12, **U5:** 161–162
    dimensions of arrays as, **U5:** 11–12, 16, 83–86, 89–91, 93–95, 100, 157–159, 173
    related pairs, **U5:** 51–52, 54–58
    relationships between, **U5:** 152, 171–172
    square numbers, **U5:** 161

Multistep problems, U8: 12, 138–141, 143–145

N

Negative changes, U8: 37–39
Negative numbers, U3: 19
Negative values
    finding difference between positive points on graph and, **U6:** 33–37, 40–41
    ordering, **U6:** 13, 30
    on temperature graphs, **U6:** 13, 27, 30, 40–41, 144–145
Nets, U9: 11, 60–63, 110
Nickel, U1: 117
Non-polyhedron, U9: 24–26, 35, 95
Notation
    for addition, **U3:** 73; **U8:** 12
    algebraic, **U1:** 17
    for arrays, **U5:** 83
    for constant rate of increase situations, **U6:** 99
    for decimals, **U7:** 98
    for division, **U5:** 13, 123, 134, 148
    for equations, **U1:** 77
    for fractions, **U7:** 38–39
    function of, **U3:** 19
    for money, **U3:** 71; **U7:** 92, 94, 98

    for multiplication, **U5:** 10, 31–33, 134, 148
    for subtraction, **U8:** 12, 43
    vertical and horizontal, **U1:** 41
Number combinations
    for 37, **U1:** 77–78
    to 100, **U1:** 117–120, 123, 137, 155–156
    for 137, **U1:** 78–84
    in addition, **U1:** 97–101, 122–123, 159–160
    equivalences, **U1:** 134–136, 167–169
    plus 1 or 2, **U1:** 162
Number composition, U1: 77–78, 134–138, 156–157, 167–169
Number line, U1: 27, 47; **U5:** 72–73, 147
    addition and subtraction on, **U1:** 16–17, 48, 129–130; **U3:** 14, 74, 98, 109–110, 116–120, 125–127, 129–135, 137–138, 143, 145–146, 148–151, 161, 164–167, 176–179, 185, 187, 193–194
    ordering numbers on, **U3:** 38–39
    representing strategies on, **U1:** 56–59, 147–148; **U3:** 79
Number order, U9: 14, 50, 55, 59
Number relationship strategy, U3: 142
Numbers
    to 1,000, **U3:** 29–33
    even and odd, **U5:** 50, 56–58
    naming and writing, **U8:** 30
    prime, **U5:** 88
    sequencing, **U3:** 31–33, 38–39
    square, **U5:** 88, 161
Number sequences
    associated with repeating patterns, **U6:** 12–13, 57–61, 63–66, 80–82, 88–89, 124–125
    associated with specific element of a repeating pattern, **U6:** 63–66, 68, 146–147
    describing, **U6:** 12–13
    extending by constant increments, **U6:** 12–13, 79–82, 88–89
Numerator, U7: 11, 25, 28
Numerical data. *See* Data.

Grade 3 Curriculum Units

U1 Trading Stickers, Combining Coins
U2 Surveys and Line Plots
U3 Collections and Travel Stories
U4 Perimeter, Angles, and Area
U5 Equal Groups
U6 Stories, Tables, and Graphs
U7 Finding Fair Shares
U8 How Many Hundreds? How Many Miles?
U9 Solids and Boxes

O

Octagonal prism, U9: 35, 95
One hundred
    as a landmark, U3: 116–120, 123–127, 139,
        143, 174, 181, 221–222
    using multiples of to solve subtraction
        problems, U3: 119–120
Ones place, U1: 40
One thousand, U3: 47–48, 191–192
Order. *See also* Sequencing. U3: 36–39
Ordering fractions, U7: 32–34
Order of operations, U1: 61
Outliers, U2: 85, 94, 130–131, 163–164,
    166–167

P

Parallelograms. *See also* Rectangles;
    Rhombuses; Squares. U4: 124–125
Patterns
    for boxes, U9: 52–54, 56–58, 60–63,
        75–79, 81–83, 86–90, 112
    for cube, U9: 110–111
    for triangular pyramid, U9: 61–63
    of temperatures, U6: 25–27, 33–34,
        41–43, 142–143
Patterns in multiples of numbers,
    U5: 49–50, 54–58, 170
Perimeter
    different shape with same perimeter,
        U4: 46–47
    of feet (irregular shape), U4: 89–92,
        96–97, 156–157
    measuring, U4: 10–11, 30–36, 38–40,
        48, 53
    ordering shapes by, U4: 47–48, 51–53
    same perimeter/different area,
        U4: 79–80, 84, 90, 96
    shapes with same area/different
        perimeter, U4: 87
Pictures, U6: 34
Place value
    to 1,000, U3: 12, 29–33, 83, 87
    addition by, U3: 88–89, 101, 191–192,
        195–197
    base-ten number system, U1: 143–144,
        153–158
    equivalence of hundreds, tens, and
        ones, U1: 86–88
    estimations and, U3: 55–56, 191–192
    number composition and, U3: 191
    recognition, U1: 37–41
    representations of, U1: 18, 27–32, 36–42,
        44, 52, 60, 65, 71, 76, 85, 130–131,
        143–146
    sequencing, U3: 36–39
    tens place, U1: 96, 102

Place-value strategy, U3: 88–89, 101,
    191–192, 195–197; U8: 10–11, 16–17,
    31–35, 37–39, 41–46, 56–60, 84, 92,
    152–153
Polygons. *See also specific polygon.*
    classification by sides, U4: 12
    perimeter of, U4: 11
    relationships among, U7: 63–64, 70–73
Polyhedron. *See also* Boxes; *specific*
    polyhedron.
    building, U9: 33–35, 38–41, 43–46
    properties of, U9: 10, 24–26, 95
    sorting, U9: 23–26, 107
    translating to/from two-dimensional
        shapes, U9: 10–11, 52–54, 56–58,
        60–63, 75–79, 81–84, 86–90, 110–112
    types and terminology, U9: 95
Positive changes, U8: 37–39
Prime numbers, U5: 88–89
Prisms. *See also* Cubes; Rectangular prisms.
    U9: 26, 32, 35, 43–45, 51–54, 56–57,
    62, 75–79, 86–90, 95, 109–110
Products, U5: 11–12, 29, 36–37, 93
Proof. *See also* Justification. U8: 168–170
Properties
    associative property
        of addition, U3: 18–19
        of multiplication, U5: 16, 40, 66–70,
          72
    commutative property
        of addition, U3: 18–19
        of multiplication, U5: 12, 16, 85
    distributive property of multiplication,
        U5: 12, 16–17, 102
    of cubes, U9: 45
    of non-polyhedron vs. polyhedron,
        U9: 10, 24–26
    of rectangular prisms, U9: 10–11, 23,
        43, 45
Pyramids. *See also specific type of pyramid.*
    U9: 10, 23, 26, 61–62, 95

Q

Quadrilaterals. *See also* Parallelograms;
    Rectangles; Rhombuses; Squares;
    Trapezoids.
    identifying, U4: 12
Quarter, U1: 117
Questionnaires, U2: 32
Questions for surveys
    with categorical data, U2: 56–57,
        157–158, 184
    with numerical data, U2: 87–88, 98–101

R

Range, U2: 85–86, 93, 130, 163, 166–167,
    U6: 40–41
Rate of change. *See also* Constant rate of
    change. U6: 16–17, 89–91
Rational numbers, U7: 10–12
Reasoning, U6: 17; U7: 12; U8: 106, 125, 129,
    168–170
Rectangles. *See also* Squares.
    area of less one corner, U4: 84, 90, 93, 96
    attributes of, U4: 12, 117, 120–122
    measuring area, U4: 65–67, 69–70
    perimeter of, U4: 11, 51
    same perimeter/different area,
        U4: 79–80, 84, 90, 96
Rectangular prisms, U9: 43–45
    determining volume with cubes, U9: 96
    patterns for open boxes for,
        U9: 52–54, 56–58, 60–61, 75–79,
        86–87, 110–112
    properties of, U9: 10–11, 23, 43, 45, 95
    volume of, U9: 11
Reflections. *See* Flips.
Related problems, U1: 99; U3: 173, 180, 197;
    U5: 60–62, 65–66, 126–128, 135,
    138–139; U8: 16–19, 43–45, 52, 56–58,
    60
Removal problems, U3: 183–184, 203;
    U8: 11, 119, 124–127, 129–131,
    138–141, 160
Repeated addition, U5: 26, 31, 36–38,
    40, 78
Repeating patterns
    of body movements, U6: 57–58
    comparing different rates of increase/
        different starting amounts, U6: 87,
        93–94, 106–107, 109–111, 148–149,
        152–154
    comparing different rates of increase/
        same starting amount, U6: 94–96,
        104–105, 152–154
    comparing same rate of increase/
        different starting amounts,
        U6: 89–91, 152–154
    comparing situations with tables,
        U6: 86–91, 93–94, 128–129, 148–151
    constant rate of change, U6: 100–102
    examining a specific element,
        U6: 63–66, 68, 146–147
    extending, U6: 12–13, 58–61, 63–66,
        68–69
    identifying a unit of, U6: 57
    numbered sequence of, U6: 12–13,
        57–61, 63–66, 68–69, 124–125
    rules for constant rate of change for,
        U6: 89–91, 94–96, 98–99, 125,
        150–151

Representations. *See also* Notation.
of addition problems, U1: 37–41,
126–130, 147–148, 152; U3: 14, 69–70,
74, 78–79, 193–194; U8: 66, 70
of addition-subtraction relationship,
U3: 18
of change over time, U6: 10–11, 117–118
of comparison problems,
U3: 158–161, 164–167, 171–172
of division problems, U5: 119
of fractions, U7: 41–42, 50
of frequency in data groups, U6: 117
of missing part problems, U3: 131–135
of multiples, U5: 66–70, 72–73
of multiplication, U5: 26, 145–148
of numbers, U1: 77–84, 157–158
of subtraction, U3: 15, 109–111, 176–179,
193–194; U8: 11, 18–19, 48–51,
120–121
using to combine fractions, U7: 12
Rhombuses, U4: 117; U7: 61–62, 70–73
Right angles (90°). *See* Angles.
Right triangles, U4: 108–109
Rotations. *See* Turns.
Rules
associating sequence of one element
with number, U6: 125
for constant rate of increase with a
starting amount, U6: 89–91,
98–99, 150–151
finding a general rule, U6: 13, 17, 94–96

S

Scale, U2: 12, 108
Sequencing. *See also* Order. U3: 36–39, 45
Shape Poster, U4: 82–83, 90, 96
Shapes. *See* Circles; Polygons;
Three-dimensional shapes;
Two-dimensional shapes.
Sharing problems, U5: 12–13, 117–118, 123,
163–164
Sides
classification of shapes by, U4: 12
of parallelograms, U4: 124–125, 156–157
of quadrilaterals, U4: 117, 120, 122
of triangles, U4: 105–109, 112–113
Sixths, U7: 10–12, 30–32, 42, 46, 61–68,
70–73, 113–114
Skip counting
by 2, U5: 50, 152–153
by 3 and 6, U5: 56–58, 72, 152–153
by 5 and 10, U5: 51–52, 54–55, 152–153
multiplication as, U5: 31, 36–38
on number line, U5: 147
representing multiplication as,
U5: 145–146
students' problems with, U5: 154

Skip counting strategy, U3: 30; U4: 93;
U5: 16, 17, 25, 65, 93–95, 98–99,
108–110, 119, 123, 139–140
Slides, U4: 12, 65, 76, 86, 143
Slope, U6: 17
Sorting, U9: 23–26, 107
Spatial relationships, U9: 11
Sphere, U9: 25–26, 95
Square arrays, U5: 88
Square numbers, U5: 88, 161; U8: 150
Square prism, U9: 62, 95
Square pyramid, U9: 95
Squares
area of, U4: 11, 75–77
attributes of, U4: 12, 117, 120–122
perimeter of, U4: 51
relationship to triangles, U4: 11, 77–79,
144, 155
Standard units of measure. *See* Units of
measure.
Star, U4: 51
Starter problems, U3: 91–93, 96, 101–102;
U5: 77–78, 102–103; U8: 73–76, 82
Story contexts, U3: 18–19, 183–184;
U5: 16, 67–68, 72–73, 103;
U7: 53–55, 103–106; U8: 11, 18–19,
48–53, 117–119, 124–127
Story problems, U1: 45–48, 123,
126–130; U3: 86, 167–168; U5: 17,
117–119, 122, 126–128, 138–139
Stories associated with graphs,
U6: 37–38, 45–47, 49–50, 104–105
Subtracting back strategy, U3: 149,
159–160, 165–167, 185–187, 211,
223–224; U8: 114–115, 135,
138–141, 166
Subtracting down strategy. *See*
Subtracting back strategy.
Subtraction. *See also* Difference.
of 10s and 1s, U1: 40–42, 61–64, 68–70
accuracy and efficiency, U1: 11–12
comparison problems, U3: 157–162,
164–167, 170–172, 174, 180,
203–204, 223–224; U8: 11, 103–108,
119, 160–161
expressions of, U8: 176–177
How Many Are Left? problems,
U3: 176–179
learning the facts, U8: 162
missing parts problems, U3: 204;
U8: 11, 119, 161
money problems, U8: 12–13, 124–127,
129–131, 138–141, 143–145
with multiples of 10 and 100,
U1: 31–33, 39–41; U3: 13–14, 97–98,
116–120; U8: 31–33, 37–39, 41–46,
48–53, 58–60
multistep problems, U8: 12, 138–141,
143–145

notation for, U8: 12
order of, U8: 38
order of operations, U1: 61
related problems, U3: 173, 180;
U8: 16–19, 43–45, 52, 56–58, 60
relationship to addition, U1: 57; U3: 18,
109–111, 202; U8: 12–13, 162
removal problems, U3: 203; U8: 11, 119,
124–127, 129–131, 138–141, 160
representations of, U1: 58–59;
U3: 109–111, 193–194; U8: 31–32,
48–51
strategies for, U3: 185–187, 210–211;
U8: 10–13, 17–18, 32–33, 48–53,
117–122, 124–127, 134–136, 163–164
of three-digit numbers, U3: 81–82, 87, 96,
100
travel problems, U3: 129–135, 148–151;
U8: 110–115
types of situations, U3: 14–15, 130, 157,
203–204; U8: 11, 117, 119, 160–161
U.S. Standard Algorithm, U8: 117
Sum. *See also* Addition. U8: 103–108
Survey
collecting data with, U2: 103–104
developing questions, U2: 56–57, 87–88,
98–101, 184
Symbolic notation, U6: 17, 99

T

Tables
creating/extending, U6: 86–91, 100–102,
128–129, 150–151
creating graphs from, U6: 10–13,
100–102, 104–106
finding one variable given the value of
the other, U6: 94–96
finding the general rule, U6: 94–96,
98–99
of situations of constant rate of change,
U6: 10–12, 86–91, 93–96, 98–102,
104–105, 126–129
using and interpreting, U6: 128–129
Tallies, U2: 50; U5: 119

Grade 3 Curriculum Units

U1 Trading Stickers, Combining Coins
U2 Surveys and Line Plots
U3 Collections and Travel Stories
U4 Perimeter, Angles, and Area
U5 Equal Groups
U6 Stories, Tables, and Graphs
U7 Finding Fair Shares
U8 How Many Hundreds? How Many Miles?
U9 Solids and Boxes

Temperature, U1: 13
    associating stories with, **U6:** 49–50
    below zero, **U6:** 13, 27, 30, 40–41,
        144–145
    line graphs of, **U6:** 10, 13, 26, 27–30,
        33–38, 40–43, 49–51, 117,
        119–123, 132–133, 142–143
    local, **U6:** 25
    over a day, **U6:** 41–43, 50–51, 119–123
    seasonal, **U6:** 41–43, 45, 47, 49–51,
        119–123
Tens place, U1: 39–41
Thirds, U7: 12, 27–28, 30–32, 42, 46, 55,
        61–68, 72–73, 113–114
Three-dimensional shapes. *See also*
    Boxes; Polyhedron; *specific three-*
    dimensional shape.
    non-polyhedron, **U9:** 24–26, 35, 95
    properties of, **U9:** 10, 24–26, 95
    sorting, **U9:** 23–26, 107
    translating to from two-dimensional
        shapes, **U9:** 10–11, 52–54, 56–58,
        60–63, 75–79, 81–84, 86–90, 110–112
    types and terminology, **U9:** 95
Time, U3: 113–114
Translations. *See* Slides.
Trapezoids, U4: 117; **U7:** 61–62, 70–73
Travel problems, U3: 129–135, 139,
        148–151, 205–209; **U8:** 11–12, 110–115
Triangles, U7: 61–62, 70–73
    angles of, **U4:** 12–13
    area of, **U4:** 11, 77–79, 144, 155
    attributes of, **U4:** 158–159
    identifying, **U4:** 12, 111–113
    perimeter of, **U4:** 11
Triangular prism, U9: 95
Triangular pyramid, U9: 39–41, 61–63
Trip meter, U3: 129
Turns, U4: 12, 64–65, 76, 86, 143
Two-dimensional shapes. *See also* Area;
    Attributes; Nets; Patterns; Perimeter;
    Polygons; *specific two-dimensional*
    shape. **U9:** 10–11
    circle, **U4:** 51
    classifying, **U4:** 12
    describing, **U4:** 12
    perimeter, **U4:** 47–48, 51–53
    same area/different perimeter, **U4:** 87
    same area/different shapes,
        U4: 63–67, 86–87
    same perimeter/different shapes,
        U4: 79–80, 84, 90, 96
    star, **U4:** 51
    translating to three-dimensional
        shapes, **U9:** 10–11, 52–54, 56–58,
        60–63, 75–79, 81–84, 86–90, 110–112
Two-step money problems, U8: 138–141,
        143–145

U

Units of measure, U2: 125–127
    for area, **U4:** 11, 75
    equivalents, **U4:** 24
    metric, **U2:** 126; **U4:** 10, 23–25, 30, 32, 137
    size of units/count of units, **U4:** 34
    using appropriate size, **U4:** 30
    U.S. standard, **U4:** 10, 23–25, 30
U.S. Standard Algorithm, U8: 84, 117
U. S. standard system. *See* Units of
    measure.

V

Values, U2: 130–131, 151–153, 164
    graphing of, **U6:** 10, 30, 42–43, 100, 118
    maximum/minimum, **U6:** 25, 29, 33–37,
        40–41
    negative
        finding difference between positive
            points on graph and, **U6:** 33–37,
            40–41
    ordering, **U6:** 13, 30
    on temperature graphs, **U6:** 13, 27, 30,
        40–41, 144–145
Variables, U6: 10, 13, 17, 30, 42-43, 89–91,
        94–96, 98–100, 118, 125, 150–151
Vertical axis, U6: 10, 30, 42–43, 100, 118
Vertices, U4: 105, 108, 111–112, 117; **U9:** 30,
        44, 95
Volume, U9: 11, 71–73, 75–79, 96

X

X-axis, U6: 10, 42–43, 100, 118

Y

Y-axis, U6: 10, 30, 42–43, 100, 118

Z

Zero, U5: 103, 161

Grade 3 Curriculum Units

U1 Trading Stickers, Combining Coins
U2 Surveys and Line Plots
U3 Collections and Travel Stories
U4 Perimeter, Angles, and Area
U5 Equal Groups
U6 Stories, Tables, and Graphs
U7 Finding Fair Shares
U8 How Many Hundreds? How Many Miles?
U9 Solids and Boxes